PUFFIN E

MOTHERSTONE

Maurice Gee is one of New Zealand's best-known writers, for both adults and children. He has won a number of literary awards, including the Wattie Award, the Deutz Medal for Fiction, and the New Zealand Fiction Award. He has also won the New Zealand Children's Book of the Year Award. In 2003 he received an inaugural New Zealand Icon Award and in 2004 he received a Prime Minister's Award for Literary Achievement.

Maurice Gee's novels include the *Plumb* trilogy, *Going West*, *Prowlers*, *Live Bodies* and *The Scornful Moon*. He has also written a number of children's novels, the most recent being *The Fat Man*, *Orchard Street* and *Hostel Girl*.

Maurice lives in Wellington with his wife Margareta, and has two daughters and a son.

Also by Maurice Gee

The O Trilogy

MOTHERSTONE

MAURICE GEE

PUFFIN BOOKS

PUFFIN BOOKS
Published by the Penguin Group
Penguin Group (NZ), 67 Apollo Drive, Rosedale, North Shore 0632,
New Zealand (a division of Pearson New Zealand Ltd)
Penguin Group (USA) Inc., 375 Hudson Street,
New York, New York 10014, USA
Penguin Group (Canada), 90 Eglinton Avenue East, Suite 700, Toronto,
Ontario, M4P 2Y3, Canada (a division of Pearson Penguin Canada Inc.)
Penguin Books Ltd, 80 Strand, London, WC2R 0RL, England
Penguin Ireland, 25 St Stephen's Green,
Dublin 2, Ireland (a division of Penguin Books Ltd)
Penguin Group (Australia), 250 Camberwell Road, Camberwell,
Victoria 3124, Australia (a division of Pearson Australia Group Pty Ltd)
Penguin Books India Pvt Ltd, 11, Community Centre,
Panchsheel Park, New Delhi - 110 017, India
Penguin Books (South Africa) (Pty) Ltd, 24 Sturdee Avenue,
Rosebank, Johannesburg 2196, South Africa
Penguin Books Ltd, Registered Offices: 80 Strand, London, WC2R 0RL, England

First published in 1985 by Oxford University Press
First published in Puffin Books, 1988
This edition published in 2005
10 9 8 7 6 5 4 3 2

Copyright © Maurice Gee, 1985

The right of Maurice Gee to be identified as the author of this work in terms of
section 96 of the Copyright Act 1994 is hereby asserted.
All rights reserved

Printed in Australia by McPherson's Printing Group

ISBN 978 0 143 31835 4
A catalogue record for this book is available
from the National Library of New Zealand.

www.penguin.co.nz

For E and A
a last look at O

Contents

CHAPTER ONE

Osro

On the afternoon of the first day Osro and his ten companions travelled without concealment on the cart road leading east. It took them through the fringes of the town, where they broke into a shop and stole jerkins and trousers and deer-hide boots, and shed their white priest-suits, and dressed as townsfolk. Several of the younger ones wept at the change. They had been ordained only a short time and now the glory of priesthood was taken from them. They lacerated their faces and wailed at their shame, until Osro spoke with a bitter kindness: 'Everything is changed. There are no more priests. But we will take this land. No one else shall have O. We have the means. Silence now. Our priest lives are done with.' And when one cried his grief a further time Osro knocked him down and threatened him with a knife. 'Another sound and you die. There is no place for weaklings.'

They buried their suits in a forest clearing beside the road, and climbed a hill and looked back at the town and the Temple and arena. Birdfolk wheeled in the sky and the cheering of the crowd made a sound like waves on a beach. Men ran on the road between the Temple and the arena, waving flags painted with a new emblem, an O.

'They think they are free,' Osro said. 'They listen to speeches. And dream of parliaments. Let them dream.'

'Master,' said a man, 'what of your Weapon? We had no time —'

'The formula is hidden in my cell. None will find it.'

'But the secret?'

'Locked in my skull. And in the Hotlands I will find an army.'

'Master, Birds in the sky.' He pointed at three Birdfolk warriors flying heavily down from the mountains towards Sheercliff.

Osro twisted his mouth. 'Yes, they come. The old life is over. These vermin infest our land. But do not fear. Remember now, we are in the guise of Freemen. We travel on our business. But soon we will take a hostage they dare not harm. Then there will be no need for pretence.'

He said no more, knowing the value of mystery and silence. His was the darkest, subtlest mind in O.

They turned their backs on the Temple and travelled all that day and all the next. The cart road petered out and they followed hunting trails in the bush. A man, Steen, a woman, Slarda, a girl, Greely, had been warrior priests. They made crossbows and killed deer and birds and the fugitives ate well on the their eastward march. On the fourth day a Woodlander girl approached with gifts – 'To mark,' she said, 'the new friendship between Woodlanders and Humans' – and Osro smiled wolfishly, and took the gifts, and made a sign to Slarda, who shot her down. 'I make no pact with vermin,' Osro said. 'Bury her. Birds must not see.'

Two days later, as they climbed into the mountains, Bird Warriors swooped down and hung over them with arrows notched on their bowstrings. 'Who are you? Where do you travel?'

Osro answered boldly: 'We are free men and women of the land. Birds do not rule us. Go your way.'

'Why do you carry crossbows?'

'To hunt our food. Why do your carry bows?'

The Warrior Bird answered less certainly: 'We patrol these lands by order of the Council of Freemen. The priesthood is outlawed and defeated. We hunt down renegade priests who murder in the lowlands and in Wildwood. And there are packs of dogs running wild.'

'We have seen none,' Osro answered. 'We are townsfolk who left the Temple when the High Priest fell. We have heard of good land north and east and travel there to make our lives. We would be farmers and live in peace.'

'Go in peace then,' said the Warrior Bird. 'But watch for outlaws. Most are in the swamps where the battle was fought, but some travel eastwards.'

'What news of the battle?' Osro cried.

'The priest army is scattered. The Candidates are banished or dead. And a free Council rules from the Temple.' The Birdfolk wheeled and swung away south over Wildwood.

'By Susan, we will rule. Priests will come again,' Steen said softly.

'No,' Osro said. 'No more priests. That game is done. When I sit on my throne the Temple will be a palace. And my name will not be High Priest — it will be King.'

'But Susan? Holy Susan?' Slarda stammered.

'A human girl. A tale for children. For peasant women sitting by their fires. Learn the new lesson. Osro is King. I shall rule by fear and might — because I desire it and because I know the way. And you ten are my fingers, and you will twist and wring.' He looked at the Birdfolk, tiny dots over the forest. 'And when I rule I'll tear the wings off Birds the way boys tear the wings off flies.'

'But what if Susan comes again?'

Osro smiled. 'Trust me. I have thought of it. She will not come. Steen, you know these hills?'

'Yes, Master. I led hunting bands here when I was young.'

'Are we close to the cave? Susan's door?'

'Half a day. But none go there. The place is forbidden.'

'Not to me. Lead the way.'

'But, Master . . .'

Osro struck him. He drew a knife and held it at Steen's throat. 'Am I your Leader?'

'Yes. Yes.'

'Then obey me. And know this, know it every one of you, and know it every man and woman and child on the planet O. I am King. Osro is King. And what I say, men do. Or they die.'

'Yes, Master.' The force of Osro's certainty overwhelmed Steen. He could not fight. His life had been obedience and faith; and now he gave himself to Osro. Joy, a new strength, filled him. 'I am yours.' He turned his eyes on the others. 'Kneel to him. He is King.'

They too were simple folk, taught obedience all their lives, and used to cruelty; and recently they had been shamed. So they knelt, and were lifted up with a new belief. 'King,' they said, trying out the word, 'Osro is King.'

'Now, stand up,' Osro said. 'Take me to Susan's door. You are my hands and I am your head. Soon O will be ours.'

They climbed higher, labouring through the middle of the day, and came to a plateau of rock. A jagged cave opened in the cliff.

'There,' Steen whispered, 'that is it. Susan's door that leads to Earth. So the legend says.'

'It is fact, not legend,' Osro said. 'Do not kneel.'

'Master, will you lead us there? To Earth?'

'No. We stay on O. When I am King we will close this door. We need no Earth. But now, we must wait for one who does.'

'Perhaps she has passed this way already.'

Osro shook his head. 'We have travelled fast. None are ahead of us. Leave no traces here. We will wait in the cave.'

'How long, Master?'

'As long as we need.'

He led them to the opening and they passed inside. They

were used to moving in darkness and they crept along the cave with no sound of foot or rattle of knife. Osro led them deep, then stopped on the inner side of a mound of stones. 'Here. Steen, go back. Wait at the mouth. Bring us warning.'

'Yes, Master.' He was gone. The others squatted by the walls of the cave and gnawed food from their satchels.

'You will dine on scented flesh in my halls,' Osro said. 'And these men who call themselves free will crawl on their knees to wait on you.'

They squatted in the dark and dreamed of it. Soon Steen came back. 'Master, they come. The two from Earth. Birds are with them.'

'Birds will not enter the cave. Quiet. Wait.'

They heard sounds far away, like whispers down a corridor. Then came a crying of farewells.

'The Birds are leaving.'

'Quiet,' Osro said. 'Our two will come.'

They heard stones disturbed by uncertain feet, and the brushing of hands on the wall, and voices that whispered because it seemed whispering was natural in the dark. A sound of quiet laughter. Talk of home. Names were spoken. Nick, one was called. The other, Susan.

'Not long now,' the boy said. 'I hope they've got some Christmas pudding left.'

'I want strawberries and cream,' said the girl.

Osro smiled in the dark. He bared his teeth.

13

CHAPTER TWO

Stinkweed

They felt their way, Shy flowers in their palms. The perfume was as faint as if it came from secret glades. O began to seem far away to Susan. This cave was almost a part of Earth. Strawberries and cream, she thought, trying not to be sad. The priests were beaten, the rule of the Temple was over, and Susan Ferris was a name that meant just Susan Ferris, nothing more. She could go home and be someone ordinary again. How horrible, she thought, to have people praying to you, and making secret signs, and rattling bones. She had done a good job getting rid of that.

'I'll miss Soona,' she said, remembering her friend.

'I'll miss Jimmy and Ben. I'd like to have a bear for a pet instead of dogs.'

'Ben wasn't Jimmy's pet. He was a friend.' The old man and the Varg were still out there, heading south. 'I wonder if the Bloodcat got back home.' He was heading north.

'He might be in here,' Nick said. 'It smells like it, anyway. Joke, joke.' But there was a rancid odour they had not noticed in the cave before.

'Something's using it.'

'Maybe for a den. We'd better go quickly. Rocks here. Watch your step.'

She climbed them nervously, feeling with her free hand. She heard Nick scrambling down the other side. His breath came heavily. But something was wrong. She had not been aware of the cave as a menacing place, simply as somewhere dark that you got out of quickly. Now it seemed to close in as though it were swallowing them. 'Nick, I don't like it.'

'Let's get to the end.'

'It smells of people. Sweat.'

'Yeah, like a football team. We'd better be gone before they come back.'

'Who are they?'

'Runaway priests, maybe. They're probably out hunting. Lucky for us.'

'Where are you?'

'Here.'

She felt her way down the pile, running her hand on the wall, and came to a firmer footing. She reached out and touched Nick. 'Maybe we should use the Shy now.'

'Better not. We've always gone to the end. No one's here.'

'Yes. All right.' She put out her hand to the wall. This time it fell on something soft; something breathed on her fingers. She jerked her hand back. A mouth, a nose! She screamed and tried to run, and heard feet rattling stones. The cave was full of people, they seemed to spring out of the walls.

'Run,' Nick yelled. She heard him fighting. 'Use your Shy.'

But it was gone, knocked from her hand, and arms came wrapping round her legs and body, round her throat. They smothered her, leathery and strong. Nick was yelling, but a blow like the thudding of an axe silenced him. Susan tried to bite the hand on her mouth. A man screeched, but the hand came back at once, on her throat.

'Stop wriggling or you're dead.'

She stopped. There were too many arms holding her. She felt moist breathing on her cheeks and sensed eyes looking at her, and felt fingers running on her face, studying it. 'Yes,' a new voice said, 'Susan Ferris. My fingers know. I looked, though she did not look at me. None gave Osro a thought. Now they will think of nothing else.'

It was not a voice Susan knew, but it had a coldness that

15

made her think of Odo Cling and brought the terror that he was alive and had captured her. 'Who . . .' she said, and could go no further.

'Osro,' said the voice. 'That is all. I have a use for you, Susan Ferris.' His fingers pinched her cheeks painfully.

'Please. Let me go home. Let us go.'

'Home?' Osro said. 'There is no home. That is not a word you can use,' and it appalled her, this second echo of Odo Cling. He too had said home had no meaning. 'Nick,' she cried, and heard him answer in a groggy voice, 'I'm all right. I lost my Shy.'

'Who are they, Nick?'

'I don't know.' She heard him struggle, heard the same dull blow. It made her ache inside.

A woman's voice said, 'Master?' and Susan had some hope, that a woman was here. But the voice said, 'We have the girl. Do we need the boy? Shall we kill him now?'

'Keep him a while. He may be useful. Bind them. Carry them out. We must head north away from Birds. Although it does not matter so much now. We have our hostage.'

'Please,' Susan said, 'we don't live here. We live on Earth. Let us go.'

'Gag them if they talk.'

Susan had a horror of gags, she thought she would suffocate, so she said no more but listened for sounds of Nick. She felt so sick with fright, and so appalled to have home snatched away and this horror, this dark side of O suddenly back, that she wondered if she were blacking out. Someone tied cords round her ankles and wrists. Hands lifted her and dragged her over the rubble. Then a man hoisted her like a sack and laid her over his shoulder. Her head banged on his back as he walked in the cave. She heard him humming a tune and recognized it as a priest song, triumphal chant, and knew that she had fallen into the hands of fugitive priests. She knew how they must hate her. Osro spoke sharply and the man fell silent. Osro? Who was he? A priest, that much was certain. But she could not remember any priest with that deadly voice. She could not believe he would let her go – or even keep her alive very long.

They came out of the cave and she twisted to see Osro, but the leather jerkins and brown leather caps were all the same. The sun had gone down over the sea, and the sky, a pale yellow, seemed cold and empty. Yellowclaw and Silverwing were down there, over Wildwood, flying away – ten minutes gone, but too far. Even if she called they would not hear. She tried to look at Nick and saw his legs dangling down the front of the man following her. His bare calves and tied ankles looked thin and pathetic.

'Put me down. I can walk. Please untie me.'

No one answered. It seemed they were frightened of being seen by Birdfolk and they hurried over the plateau to the path leading down the hill. They loped along and Susan's head banged sharply and the man's bony shoulder cut into her. Several times they changed. She was slung from one to another like a roll of carpet. Nick was transferred too. She glimpsed his face, with blood on his forehead. Nick would fight. He would always fight. But nothing would help them now. Woodlanders, Birdfolk, Jimmy, Ben – no one was near.

It grew dark. Their pace was slower. But they did not stop. She heard the man leading call soft instructions. His name was Steen. Always he spoke to Osro, calling him Master, and the others, when they spoke, used that name too. Who was he? He spoke of having seen her so he must be from the Temple. But she could not remember any but the High Priest noticing her. Not until the moment in the arena, when she had stood on the dais and told them to take off their Ferris bones — they had looked then. But if Osro had been there he was one of thousands.

The men slung her onto a shoulder that hurt less. She heard Nick groan as they changed him over. The journey went on, down steep slopes and over shingle slides, where her bearer had trouble keeping his feet. Then they walked beside water. She heard wind in trees and the call of the night bird that sounded like a morepork. Later, they seemed to be in a gorge for something black blotted out the sky on either side and left a band of stars overhead. Clouds covered them, and rain fell, wetting her back. It came up the gorge on the wind, but a turning gave them shelter, and Steen led them on to a bank of pebbles under a cliff.

'It is midnight, Master. Will this place do?'

'Yes,' Osro said. 'Feed them. Don't waste too much on the boy.'

Her bearer lowered her gently enough. She supposed he had orders not to hurt her, but Nick was thrown down roughly. She heard him grunt as his back struck the pebbles. She wriggled towards him. 'Nick, are you all right?' He looked at her as though he had just woken from sleeping badly and could not remember the face leaning over him. The whites of his eyes shone in the dark, then disappeared as his head fell forward.

'Please,' she said to Osro, 'let me look after him.'

Osro made a signal and a man unpicked the knots at her ankles and wrists. Her hands took a moment to come alive, then she untied Nick, tearing her nails on the cords. His head lolled but when she rubbed his hands to warm them he half opened his eyes. He made a warning tilt of his head at the man beside them. She knelt closer and pretended to support him on her shoulder.

'I'm not as bad as I'm making out,' he muttered.

'Nick — '

'Don't say anything. Get me down to the water to drink.'
He raised his eyes piteously to the man and croaked, 'Water.'

'Please,' Susan said, 'can I take him down?'

The guard looked at Osro. She could not see the leader's face, even though men had a fire of twigs burning at the base of the cliff.

'Do nothing foolish. If one of you tries to run I'll kill the other.'

She helped Nick up and they went the few metres to the creek, sliding in the shingle. The guard stood at the top of the bank, watching them. They knelt at the water and drank and washed. Then Susan bathed Nick's face. She ladled handfuls of water on the cut on his cheekbone. 'Hurts,' he winced.

'It needs a stitch.'

'Too late now. Listen, I'm not bad. I'm pretending. But I don't think they'll keep me alive very long.'

'Who are they?'

'Runaway priests. They'll use you as hostage to get away. And sell you for ransom. To Kenno.'

'Osro – the leader – he calls himself king.'

'There's probably lots of people playing king. They're only crooks. But they're dangerous.'

'You've got to get away.'

'I know. One's got a better chance than two. I'll bring the Birdfolk. And Jimmy. And Ben.'

'How?'

'I've got my Shy. I only said I lost it. It's in my pocket.'

'When will you try?'

'Not tonight. I'm not fit enough. My head aches. Pretend to help me up.'

She supported him up the shingle bank. Osro, silhouetted against the fire, watched them come. He turned into a shelter of stakes and blankets and Susan saw food taken in to him. They crept close to the fire. No one offered coverings but the woman Slarda thrust strips of meat at them and they ate hungrily. Susan had two strips and tried to share with Nick, who had only one, but Slarda knocked him away. She drew her finger across her throat. They were aching to kill him and Susan wondered how long it would be. Not tonight or they would not have fed him.

She looked at the women. Apart from Slarda, who was long-boned and stringy, the other three were not much older than her. They might have come from Earth, they would have looked at home on a beach, or counting out money in a bank. Ordinary-looking. Until you saw their eyes. There was one who looked like Susan's phys. ed. mistress at school, but when she turned the likeness vanished. Her eyes were deadly, with pointed flames reflected from the fire. She hated Susan and wished her dead, and her lips gave a savage curl, and she felt for the bones that had hung on her breast and clenched her fist to find them gone. There would be no help from the women, and the unnaturalness of it turned Susan cold. She huddled against Nick.

'Sleep,' Slarda said, but offered nothing to lie on. They lay down side by side on the stones, as close to the fire as they could get, and tried to rest. They dozed and turned and dozed through the night, and woke in the dawn stiff and cold. The priests – ex-priests, outlaws – were packing for the march, but Steen came from Osro's shelter and told them to wait. 'The Master has much to plan.' So they ate again and sat waiting under the cliff. Rain still fell in the gorge and the creek was higher. Steen walked down and watched it, and came back with a worried face. 'We'll be trapped in here if we don't move soon.'

'Good,' Nick whispered to Susan.

'How do you feel?'

'Dizzy. If I'm going to get away I'll have to go soon.'

But they sat there all through the morning and he found no chance. Slarda had put the fire out. The air was warm and the rain fell thick and straight. Sheets of water streamed from the cliff, closing the hollow like a room. Steen broke through it now and then and looked at the river. It moved stones on the shingle bank, making them grind like teeth. But still Osro gave no order to move. The guards sat watching Nick and Susan. They had the priest habit of not blinking and spoke in the voice trained for temple chants and striking fear. Slarda filed heads for crossbow bolts. She tested them on her thumb.

There had been no breakfast for Nick and Susan but lumps of bread were handed them at noon. Again Nick got less than Susan. They drank water from the sheet streaming from the cliff and she managed to give him a crust she had saved.

'I'll have to get somewhere with just one guard,' Nick whispered.

'Will the Shy knock him out?'

'It better. It worked with the Halfmen.'

'These aren't Halfmen, Nick.'

'They hate the Shy. They call it stinkweed. So maybe it smells different to them.'

'I hope so.'

Slarda jerked them back to the base of the cliff and thrust them down. They had settled only a moment when Steen came out of the shelter and said, 'The Master will talk with them.' He led them to the opening in the blankets and pushed them in. It was darker inside and the man called Osro was like an animal squatting at the back of a den. He had no trouble seeing, for he worked at papers on his knee, making tiny marks with a charcoal stick. Steen forced them down. 'Kneel,' he said.

21

They stayed on their knees while Osro worked. He made more marks and gave a laugh. 'Do you know what I am doing, Susan Ferris?' He looked at her suddenly, with eyes pale in the gloom.

'No,' she whispered.

'Each of these marks is a part, an ingredient, and when I have gathered them all, in the right measures and right weights, and bring them carefully face to face I have a Weapon. A Weapon like none that has ever been. With it I shall rule, O is mine. So you see, it does not matter that the Temple is finished. I would have torn it down anyway, with all its foolishness of painted faces and sacrifice. I need only this. No Susan Ferris. Or priests, or bones. But still, you are useful for a time.'

Susan wet her lips. She felt the power locked in him, the belief in himself. 'Who are you?' she managed to say.

'You don't know me? Even yet?'

'No.'

He smiled. Then he raised his hands in front of his chest and let them dangle from the wrist. He loosened his mouth and made his eyes roll. He set up a tuneless nasal humming. And Susan knew him.

'You. The Candidate. The one who was mad.'

Osro laughed. He let his hands fall. 'Good, good. You're a clever girl, as my friend the High Priest said.'

'You weren't mad at all.'

'I was sane. The High Priest was mad. I acted my part for seven years, and stayed alive while the others died. Do you know how long they lasted? Two, three turns. Three was the longest. Except for me. I flattered him. He looked at me and saw the extent of his power.'

'But we saved you. We saved you from that.'

'You interfered. I need no help. I was ready to have him killed. Then I would have been High Priest.'

'But the guard. The one behind you with a sword.'

'He was mine. I controlled him. Look at me Susan.'

She did. She saw his cold pale eyes. 'You can hypnotize.'

'I can control, at least a mind as simple as the guard's. But I was waiting. I waited until I had my Weapon. I had done the calculations. All that was left was to get the parts. Then you came along with your Birds, with Jimmy Jaspers and his Varg – and interfered.'

She felt the anger in him, but felt his control of it. That was what made him terrifying: control. She knew he was more dangerous than the High Priest, more dangerous even than Otis Claw. He was colder, more ambitious, and less concerned with cruelty and revenge.

'What are you going to do now?'

'There are tribes in the Hotlands. I have dealings with them. I will raise an army and march south.'

'You can't win.'

'Do you think your Birds will stop me? Or your army of Freemen?' Osro smiled and tapped the paper in his hand. 'You forget my Weapon.'

'What is it?'

'The army will burn like a field of dry corn. And the Birds will flare in the sky like paper kites.'

'It's some sort of ray gun,' Nick said.

'Ah, the boy. He speaks. You will never see it, Nicholas Quinn. And you, Susan Ferris, I need you only until I reach my tribes. So,' he turned to Steen, 'take them away. I will work another hour. Then we will go.'

'The river is rising, Master.'

'Tell me when we are no longer safe.' He dismissed them with a flick of his hand.

Outside, the rain had thinned to a drizzle. It filled the gorge like smoke. The river was bucking and surging. It beat on the cliff opposite and turned with a writhing twist

fifty metres down and vanished round a bend as if
something swallowed it. Logs and trees floated by and a
drowned animal like a moose rammed into the cliff and
turned over slowly with its stiff legs at the sky. The children
watched until it went from sight.

'The river turns west. It heads for the sea.'

'When you get away, follow it,' Susan said. She looked
at him and tried to smile. She did not think he would get
away.

'I've got to tell Kenno and the Birdfolk about this
Weapon.'

'Yes.' But she wondered if Osro had hypnotized her. She
did not believe the ex-priest could be beaten.

The guards made ready to start. At last Osro came out
of his shelter. Two men packed the blankets and tied them
on their backs. Everything was ready.

'Master,' Steen said, 'we will cross this shingle bank and
turn up the hill away from the river. Then we can strike
across the uplands to the Belt.'

'Lead, then,' Osro said. 'But first, kill the boy.'

'Yes, Master.' Steen started towards Nick, where he stood
with Susan in the back of the hollow. But a young woman
sprang in front of him. 'Steen, let me. Let me do it.'

'No, me,' cried another, pushing foward. She drew her
knife and ran at Nick. Steen knocked her aside. He gave
a shout of anger.

'The Master spoke. He ordered me. Will you disobey?'
He stood in front of Nick and Susan, facing the guards,
who leaned at them, almost panting in their eagerness. Steen
held them off, and Osro watched, smiling, stroking his chin.
Susan had a moment to think. The order for Nick's death
had come so suddenly it had frozen him. But she
remembered his plan of getting alone with a guard. Steen
turned at last and looked at Nick, and she flung herself at

him, clutched his shirt. 'No, please, I don't want to see. Take him somewhere else. Please. Please.' She felt tears running on her face, but she heard Osro laugh and heard his voice: 'Do what she asks. We must keep her happy for a time. Take him back along the path.'

She saw Nick's face, white, dark-eyed. He had time only for a glance at her before Steen gripped his collar and forced him away, but the nod he gave was a way of thanking her. Steen pushed him through the guards and dragged him along the shingle bank. They went behind a rock leaning over the river. A moment passed. Another.

'He takes his time,' said the girl called Greely.

'He is too old,' grumbled another.

The water roared and the shingle growled, but no sound came from behind the rock.

'Master?' Slarda said.

'See,' Osro nodded.

There was no need. Steen crawled from behind the rock, his faced raised, mottled red and white, and his eyes blind. He tried to stand, but fell and rolled on his back, clawing at the sky. His voice howled above the sound of the river.

Guards ran to help him. Others darted behind the rock.

'The boy had stinkweed,' Slarda cried. 'He used it on Steen. He is gone.'

'Find him.'

They were so busy with Steen and so headlong in their search along the path they did not see Nick. Susan saw him. He had gone the most unexpected way. She saw a tree come bucking down the river, its green head billowing like a sail, and there was Nick hidden in the branches, riding past not twenty metres away. He clung like a possum as the tree rolled. It slammed into the cliff opposite and the force of the water made it rear. It was as if the tree was growing again, lifting Nick with it. Then it plunged and was buried and the roots showed in the air, pink and brown. Still Nick clung in the branches. She saw his face flash white. Slarda saw it too. She had climbed on the rock to scan the path and saw Nick as she turned to cry to Osro. She gave a yell and unslung her crossbow. The others saw where she was looking. The tree had turned again and was racing away from the cliff towards the bend in the river. But Nick was exposed in the branches and could not move for fear of losing his hold. Slarda levered back the cord of her bow and slammed a bolt in the groove. Susan saw her grinning fiercely. The shot was forty metres, easy for her. Nick watched helplessly. Holding on with arms wide, he seemed to offer himself.

No one watched Susan. She moved behind Osro and picked up a stone the size of a cricket ball. She was no good at throwing but knew that Nick was dead if she missed and the knowledge swelled Slarda's face like a balloon, brought it close. It was as if she had simply to reach out and push the stone. Osro saw too late what she was doing. He lunged at her and knocked her down and put his foot on her. But the stone was gone. It curved in the air, slow as a football. Susan saw Slarda sight her bow. And that was all. A cry. The twang of a bowstring. Then a glimpse, a last one: the green tree sailing on the river, and Nick riding high, going from sight, going to safety.

Osro ground her with his foot. Slarda stood over her with bleeding face. 'Let me kill her, Master.'

'No. Take one other. Hunt the boy. See him dead.'

'Master,' someone said, 'he has taken Steen's knife.'

'It does not matter,' Slarda said, 'I have my bow.'

'And later, when I have no use for this,' Osro kicked Susan, 'she is yours.'

Slarda's eyes shone. She gave a short quick bow, called harshly to Greely, and they were gone.

'Now, Susan Ferris. Stand and walk,' Osro said.

She obeyed. She walked between two guards along the shingle and climbed a track leading into hills, away from the river. Osro led. Two men came last, carrying Steen in a litter made of blankets. They went on through the drizzling rain, through the afternoon into night. She felt as if she was going deeper and deeper into a nightmare and the only thing that kept her in touch with the normal world was the thought of Nick riding to freedom on a tree.

She ate. She drank. She lay down to sleep; and did not know whether she dreamed Slarda standing in the dawn with Osro, and her voice saying, 'It is done. The boy is dead.'

CHAPTER THREE

'Use yer loaf'

He saw Slarda reel from the impact of the stone and the bolt from her crossbow flash across the river and rebound from the cliff. Susan was down, under Osro's foot, and he screamed at the man to let her go. Then the tree bucked and almost threw him. It swung round the bend in the river and he saw water beating on rocks ahead. The tree gathered speed. He yelled with fear and burrowed into the branches. The roots struck the rapids as though crashing into a wall. The blow ripped one of his hands from the branch. The tree made a half turn, slamming into a boulder, lurching away. But a weight of water pressing on his back kept Nick in place. He got his hold again and rose on his legs to ride the tree. He must be part of it. He must bend with the branches.

The gorge went on and on like a chute. Hidden rocks made dragon-backs, whale-backs, rearing horses, in the water. The tree rode some and slouched through others. Nick moved his grip and jumped from side to side to keep his weight even. Water broke on him and punched and stretched him. He did not think he could hold on much longer.

The gorge opened out and hills sloped up on the left and right, covered with bush. Trees leaned into the water and broke it into eddies and back-currents. Nick tried to steer at the left-hand bank – away from the side where guards would be coming with their crossbows – but the tree would not answer. It kept in the middle, turning over with a corkscrew motion. The hills began to close in. Another gorge, another chute, was coming. Its narrow hungry mouth was full of spray.

Nick rode through. He was beaten with water, half-drowned. The branches of the tree were stripped of leaves and the bark on the trunk was shredded. Then another stretch opened up, between low hills. The water seemed to gallop along, rising and falling. A rock standing up from the surface turned the tree left. It sped near the bank, roots first, running easily with its foliage gone. Nick sat in the branches like a helmsman and watched for a chance to jump ashore.

Then a third gorge showed its mouth, round a bend. It was blacker, deeper, and breathed out spray like smoke from a forest fire. It seemed to draw Nick in as though it were a mouth sucking in breath. It boiled and rumbled. Great twisting melon-shapes and tongue-shapes grew in it. Cables writhed and lashed, slugs of water bounced into the air, and into it the river slid as smooth as oil running from a spout.

Nothing could survive. Nick must take whatever chance he had, take it now. He climbed out of the branches, ran three steps along the trunk, and threw himself at the bank ten metres away. He hit the water as though running into a wall. It bounced him off and turned him over and over. Then it swallowed him. He clawed for the surface, and had a glimpse of the reeling sky, a lungful of air, then was down again. A boulder struck a club-blow on his back. He flung his arms at it but found no grip, and was tumbled into the hollow, the boiling pot, on its down-river side. Something came to join him. He thought it was alive and gave a cry. But it was the tree, pushing him with roots splayed like fingers. It freed him from the hollow but pushed him at the gorge, then turned away. He swam with fierce over-arm strokes, but felt he was falling down the river as though down a cliff. Bushes flashed by, out of reach. A smooth rock wall curved into the gorge and he slid on it as though on ice. He hooked his fingers, trying for a hold, but they ran like glass marbles on a floor.

The tree went from sight, tipping its head as though in farewell. A sound of fracturing came from the gorge. Nick grabbed again – his last chance. A bush with red flowers leaned at the water, growing from a crack in the stone. Red in this dark place was unnatural. It flashed on his eye, he lunged at it and caught his fist in a web of roots. Then he hung, body flat, hand locked in the bush. He tried to turn himself to give his other hand a better chance, but the water pulled too strongly, sucking at his legs as though trying to swallow. So he bent his elbow, drawing himself back. It took all his strength, he knew he would not manage it again. He flung his free hand over his head, clutching blindly. Something met his fingers, strong as wire. He dug, he clutched; and had two hands locked in the roots of the bush. He could lift his body. He raised himself as though on an exercise bar, forcing his head among branches. Then he freed one hand and made another grab, and had a branch as thick as the handle of a bat. He pulled again and climbed into the bush and crouched like a monkey, looking round.

There was little to see: river, hills, stone, spray. He had so strong a sense of being nowhere that dizziness overcame him and almost made him tumble into the water. Out there was emptiness, and here a tiny world a metre square, with Nick Quinn squatting in it. He gripped branches in his hands and held on tight. To make himself more real he raised his head and howled his name, but the sound was snatched away by the thunder in the gorge. Then something brushed his cheek. He drew back his head and looked at it: a red flower. That kept him sane. The bush had saved him. It was as if it had grown here just for this. He held on. It was all he had.

Later he found Steen's knife in its sheath, belted round his waist, and thinking back, was able to put people in his world. Steen, Osro, Slarda. Susan Ferris. Where was she? What were they doing to her now? He remembered his last sight of her, lying on the shingle bank, under Osro's foot. Soon, when they had no use for her, they would kill her. He could not think of anything to do. But he pulled out Steen's knife and looked at it, and remembered how the man had let him go to draw the blade. That had been his chance. He had jumped at him, the Shy flower in his palm, and struck him open-handed on the mouth. The flower was bruised and wilted, more grey than blue, but its magic was not lost. As his hand rolled wetly on Steen's mouth he felt the perfume sac burst and saw the pupils of Steen's eyes dilate. The scent of Shy wrapped round them like a blanket. It strengthened Nick, but knocked Steen to his knees. His head fell between his shoulders. He tried to raise it, tried to reach out and clasp Nick's ankle, but his muscles would not obey. He made choking sounds. Nick stepped at him and knocked him over with a heel kick. He unbuckled the belt that held the knife, tied it round his own waist. He took the man's food pouch and belted it on. Steen watched, with wide dark eyes. It was as if he had been hit with a solar plexus punch and kept his consciousness but could do nothing. He was like an insect turned on its back, moving his limbs in jerky circles. 'Listen,' Nick said softly, 'I'm going for the Birdfolk. We'll come back. If you hurt Susan you're dead. The lot of you.' It felt good saying that, and seeing the man lie there like a baby. He turned and ran and, as if the Shy had given him extra sense, had a plan at once. He ran fifty metres up the path, watching the river, saw several logs float by – then had what he wanted. He ran into the water and swam across the current, timing it, and pulled himself into the tree. Going back past the rock, he saw Steen crawling for help, and wanted to shout insults at him.

Nick grinned. He had done it perfectly. He'd got away. And got away from the rapids. Now he had to get out of this.

He put the knife in the sheath and took out a strip of meat. It was softened and bleached by water, like old bait, but he chewed and swallowed hungrily. Then he looked up to see where he must go. The bush was at the bottom of a cleft which widened into a chimney as it went up. He could not see what happened at the top. Perhaps nothing. Perhaps he was trapped here until he died. He put the thought aside and crept through the branches and wedged himself in the crack. It was too narrow for easy climbing, but he found small roughnesses and inched his way up, back to one wall, face to the other. Then the chimney widened and he was able to lever and brace himself, going star-shaped, with palms flat and ankles bent at an angle.

Near the top the chimney was too wide. But there, leaning down to help, were the roots of another bush. He climbed them like a rope ladder and came out on the top of a pillar standing like a gatepost at the entrance of the gorge. The red bushes were tangled so thickly on top he had to wriggle in like a snake. He crossed to the gorge side and put his head over the drop.

At once his face was wet with spray. It flew in the gorge like midges, luminous in the last sun from the west. The rapids went on and on, leaping on the walls. The tree Nick had ridden was caught in a fissure halfway down and seemed to have died there, leafless and grey. He saw how close he had come to dying, and shrank away and made himself small in the wet hollow on top of the pillar.

'Now,' he said to himself, 'O.K. Nick,' but did not know what to do. He crawled back to the chimney. There was no way to go further up the cliff, even if he jumped across to it. It curved towards the sky without a handhold. A sobbing came from his throat. He felt he had been cheated.

Then he saw a movement on the bank over the river. At first he thought it was an animal. It was quick, angular, furtive, grey. He recognized Slarda. Behind her came a second figure, smaller: one of the murderous girls, the one called Greely. He whimpered and shrank in the bushes.

Slarda was like a hunting dog. She ran, stopped, listened, pointed, ran. The girl followed. They were coming round to the mouth of the gorge. He saw them scrambling on boulders. Their crossbows were strapped on their backs.

Where the river ran into the gorge, Slarda stopped. Greely took her arm and leaned out, peering down the rapids. She pointed and seemed to shout. She had seen the tree wedged in the fissure. Slarda pulled her back and the girl spoke eagerly. Then they searched the cliff and pillar with their eyes. Sunlight was streaming up the gorge, making rainbows in the spray. Nick felt his face shining like an electric bulb. He rolled back and lay in the hollow. The flowers twinkled over him like stars. But he knew he had to look again. If his hunters had seen him he had to know. He raised himself on his knees and pushed his head through the branches.

They were still there, arguing what to do. Greely seemed to want to climb to the top of the gorge, but Slarda pointed back the way they had come and made an upward motion with her arm. She wanted the long way. Nick hoped she would win. It would give him more time. But time for what?

They started back, moving half bent over, with the eagerness of dogs. Nick looked down the gorge, into the light of the setting sun. It picked out a row of red bushes in the stone, below the cliff-top. They glowed like embers, and he saw at once they made a path for him — if he could take it. He wriggled across the pillar to its down-river side. The first bushes grew on the far side of a metre-wide gap — an easy jump — and others ran from it in a line slanting up, growing on a ledge a hand-span wide. If he could climb in the bushes, use them like a road, and if their roots were strong enough, he would come out on the lip of the gorge halfway along. He looked and shivered. He would be over water all the way, and if he fell, if one of the bushes broke, the rapids would take him.

One of Jimmy's sayings came to him: 'Yer don't wanter think too much, it'll melt yer brain.'

'O.K., Jimmy,' he said. He made sure his knife and food pouch were belted tightly. Then he stood on the rim of the pillar, leaned over the gap, and launched himself from his point of balance. An easy jump. But the branches were slimy. Bark slid under his fingers. He dangled by one hand, and made wild second grab with the other, and only then was safe. He pulled himself into the bush.

'Ride yer luck.' Jimmy again. He did not look down or stop to think, but climbed through the branches, close to the cliff, and pulled into the next bush — and the next. They grew so close together he could not tell which branch belonged to which. Their roots curled like fingers, holding stone. He stepped along, swung along, went like a monkey, like a crab. The water boomed. The spray, almost blinding in the light, made drops in his eyebrows, ran on his face. He licked it and felt it ease the dryness in his throat.

Slowly he came close to the lip of the gorge. It was only a room's width away. But the bushes seemed to have a harder time. They were gnarled like trees above a snow-line, some no larger than bonsai trees. He tried to grip them close to the roots, and hoped their hold was strong in the stone. 'Ride yer luck.' He let his feet dangle, swung along, then crawled up and side-stepped on the bushes like a path. They bent beneath his weight. Far below, the rapids ended and the river ran smooth between the cliffs.

The bushes stopped short. He stood on the last and saw it bend and seemed to hear its roots groan; and he felt with his fingers for the lip of the cliff. It was there, at his full stretch, and ridged so that his grip was firm. He had no strength for a straight pull up, but was able to brace himself, lean back and walk two steps, and roll on to the cliff top. He lay there panting, then pushed himself further from the drop. He did not think he could stand and walk away.

In a moment he pulled himself onto his knees. He looked round to see where he was. It was a bare rock ledge, no wider than a one-way bridge, running west. A bank of stone rose on his left to thick green bush. He turned and looked over the gorge. The gap was thirty metres with the same ledge and bank, and hills beyond. Slarda and Greely were there somewhere. But all he had to do was climb to the bush and he was safe. They would never know he had not ridden his tree into the gorge, and died in that tumble of water.

He pushed himself to his feet and stood swaying. He knew if he got too close to the gorge he would fall in. He stumbled to the bank and looked up: a simple climb, but his strength was gone. His limbs felt as though they were stuffed with wool. He leaned his arms on the bank and rested. Then something sang towards him like a wasp and struck the stone and threw splinters at him. They cut his mouth. He tasted blood.

Another singing came as he threw himself flat, and the thing, a crossbow bolt, sprang off the bank and arced over him. He jumped to his feet and ran. Slarda and Greely were scrambling from the trees over the gorge. They stopped to

35

reload, and Nick saw Slarda pause and strike the girl. In her eagerness to kill she had shot too soon. If they had crept closer they would have had him like a beetle on a wall.

But they still had him. There was no place on the bank he could climb and be in the trees before they closed up for an easy shot. So he ran. He ran on the smooth rock ledge, with the bank rising on one side and the gorge dropping away on the other. A hundred metres behind, over the gap, Slarda came, long-striding, with Greely straining ahead, yelping like a dog. Nick panted, heaved. Tears ran on his face. He had nothing left. He had done too much. They were going to kill him. The bank grew steeper, the trees seemed further away, far out of reach. He saw the place where the stone ledge ended. It stopped like a washed-out bridge. Beyond was emptiness, a drop to the river and the bush.

Another bolt sang by. The girl had tried a second shot. He heard Slarda scream angrily. She knew he had nowhere to go.

Nick stumbled and almost fell. He felt his feet falling from under him. Then he saw he was running in a depression. It was like a shallow ramp slanting down to the end of the ledge. Branches from the forest littered it. To Slarda it must seem he was sinking, knees and hips and waist, into solid stone. She gave a yell of fury. Nick looked back. Greely had reloaded as she ran. But Slarda made her stop and crouch and used her as support for a certain shot. Nick stopped and faced her, and seemed to look into the arrow head. It swelled and shrieked, coming at him. He did not duck, he simply fell over, and the bolt clipped a tuft from his hair. Strands settled on his face. He closed his eyes to stop them tickling, and spread his palms flat on the stone, thinking it was warm as a bed.

Later, he realized he had slept. The sun was deep in the

sky, touching the hills. He half-rose in panic, then calmed himself. They — Slarda, Greely — were over the gorge, they could not get him. He crawled further down the hollow. It deepened and he rose and walked in a crouch. The clouds had gone, wind died away. The still tops of trees showed over the gorge. He stepped over a rotten branch and came to the edge. The river curled lazily, hugging the cliff. It wound through wooded hills, gleaming pink from the last of the sun. There was no way down. The cliff beneath him was undercut. And he could not have climbed in any case, he was too exhausted. His head ached and his limbs were bruised from knocks taken in the river. He felt the cut on his cheek. It seemed to be washed clean, but was aching too, and he wondered if it was turning septic.

He stared into the distance, over the hills, trying to see if Birdfolk were flying there. But he could not look at the sun, halfway down behind a flat-topped hill, and he shaded his eyes and watched the river. Down there, two or three kilometres away, was a narrow place where trees leaned across the water. A hunter as eager as Greely would climb or jump or swing across somehow. He wondered if she was on her way, and knew he had to find out what was going on over the gorge.

He tried to work out where Slarda would least expect him to raise his head, and saw no place was better than any other. But he would need to be quick. One look, no more. He raised his head. And there was Slarda, forty metres away, with loaded bow and cheek-bones gleaming. She stood on the edge of the gorge and looked tall enough to step across. The girl was dragging branches from the bush.

Slarda saw Nick. She raised her bow. But he was down and the bolt whistled by. At once he stood. Slarda was reloading and Greely had her bow on her back. He had three or four seconds. He looked at the branches. They came from a resinous tree that burned like a flare. Others were piled on the ledge. A bonfire! They would light it so he could not slip away in the dark.

He sat down before Slarda could shoot. One of them would watch, one sleep. And in the morning one – the girl probably – would cross somewhere and come back and kill him. He was finished. They would not leave him alone until he was dead.

He looked west again. The sun was gone. The sky was a dark blue cave with luminous walls. Out there was the sea, beyond the hills. And south was the Temple, probably with a new name now. He would never get there. Or get to Jimmy, heading south with Ben. And Susan, heading north, would wait for help that would never come. He felt like raising his head and howling.

But what would Jimmy say? 'Quit yer blubbin'.' He wiped his face. 'Jimmy,' he said, 'I rode my luck.' Now his luck was finished. What would the old man tell him to do next? 'Use yer loaf.' 'What?' 'Use yer loaf – that thing on top of yer.' It seemed as if Jimmy *was* there in the half-light, and Nick shook his head. He did not want to start hallucinating. But Jimmy's advice was good – even if it made nonsense of his other advice. (Better anyway to melt his brain than wait for Slarda.) The only way out of this was by cunning. He turned it over, looking for a weakness in Slarda's trap. It grew darker; but suddenly the sky was light. They had lit their fire. It made a yellow dome and he was just inside the rim of it. The night beyond turned a deeper blue. They would not see him well if he ran, but they would see, with their Guy Fawkes fire.

Nick stopped at that. Guy Fawkes! He saw a figure dressed in a holey cardigan, torn boots, with wool for hair, potato for a nose, burning in the flames of a monstrous fire; and slowly he grinned, and then he laughed – which hurt his mouth. He tasted blood again, and did not care. They would not leave him alone until he was dead. So — 'use yer loaf' — he would be dead.

He crept up the hollow, found the rotten branch, hauled it back. He took off his T shirt and rolled it on the branch and pulled it down. One of the sleeves fitted on a side stump. Now — what next? He crawled back up the hollow and found a clump of wiry grass growing in a crack. He dug it out with Steen's knife, and took a lace from one of his sneakers and tied the grass on top of the branch. Hair, just the right length, and in the bad light colour would not matter. He found three chips of pale stone, and made holes in the rotten wood, and hammered in the stone with the handle of the knife. Eyes, mouth. He had a Guy: Nicholas Quinn. He hauled it to the edge of the cliff, patted it and left it lying there.

Keeping low, he scraped up an arsenal of stones. He moved along the hollow, throwing at the fire, letting Slarda and Greely glimpse him now and then. He could not throw accurately, bent double, but the important thing was to pretend he was desperate. Twice crossbow bolts hummed over his back. He threw more stones. Then he scuttled to the edge of the cliff, to his Guy. He lifted it and raised it on an angle — Nicholas Quinn peering out to see if he had scored any hits. He let it stay too long.

Thunk! Thunk! He felt the bolts jerk the Guy in his hands. Their sound was wet and murderous. At once he screamed. And cut it off. He pushed the Guy higher, leaned it over the drop, let it fall.

No sound came from over the gorge. Time passed — too much. Then, from far away, came the heavy splash of a body striking water.

Slarda gave a cry of satisfaction. Greely squealed, she sang high notes of pleasure, forgetting her priestly training in silence. The fire flared and crackled as more branches went on. They must be at the edge, Nick thought, trying to see the river and the body. But that was too far, they would not manage.

He crawled back from the drop and lay down carefully, making no sound. He did not know whether his hunters would sleep by their fire or leave at once — even search the river. It did not matter. He had no strength to care any more. All he wanted was sleep. The rock kept some warmth from the sun. He spread himself out and felt it seep into his body.

'Jimmy, I did it,' he whispered.

'Good on yer, son. Yer a bloddy bottler.'

Nick went to sleep.

CHAPTER FOUR

The Freemen of O

Nightmares: dogs with teeth like sharks, biting knee and elbow. They loped, they bounced like tennis balls, and their tongues were dripping like taps. He could not keep ahead. His legs had rusty joints, and the dogs fixed their teeth and ground on bone. Bone fingers squeezed his head, denting temples, squashing eyeballs. Light shone, flushed like water in the basin of his head. It ran into his mouth and burned it dry. Flashing head-lamps. Furnace roaring.

Time stretched out like rubber. It snapped back and stung him. How long had gone by? Why did the world turn end over end, and sea and sky close like the pages of a book? A weightless dark, a warmth like eiderdowns, and somewhere, far off, whistling wind, and creaking like the saddles of trotting horses.

He woke slowly, waking without pain. First there was purple, very dull. Then a face, white, blue-eyed, framed with hair turned like polished wood. She smiled at him and brushed liquid silver from her cheek. He was not sure she was real, but tried to speak her name, and felt the ugly dryness of his mouth. She placed her hand on it, stopped his croaking, and fed a spoon of oil between his lips. Oil like honey. It let him smile and freed his tongue.

'Soona?'

'Yes, Nick. Nicholas Quinn. We had no time to talk in the arena, but I remember how you ran to save us, and how you faced the Priest, and conjured up the Birdfolk in the sky. It has been a great joy to nurse you back to health.'

'Am I – is this – are we in the Temple?'

41

'Yes. Though we call it by other names. It is Hall. Hall of Justice. People's Hall.'

'And this – this room?'

'Is where the priests kept me prisoner. Where Susan climbed with the stone-silk gloves.'

'Have you found her?'

'Oh, Nick. Even in your sickness you told us where to go. Words all broken up, but we put them together. Birdfolk went out – Silverwing and Yellowclaw, and hundreds, hundreds. Birdfolk.'

'And? Did you find her?'

'Once. Once she was there. And then she was gone. And seen no more. But they are searching. If she can be found they will find her.'

He saw from her grieving face she did not believe it. She placed her hand on his forehead, where it lay cool as stone. 'Don't talk any more. You must sleep. Perhaps when you wake we'll have news.' She tried to smile, but a new tear trickled on her face. 'I knew her only one day and a half, but in that time she became my sister.'

'What do you mean, was there, then was gone?'

'When you wake the Birdfolk will be returned. They will tell you.'

'How did they find me? How long have I been here? Let me up. I've got to find her.'

He tried to climb out of the bed but found he was too weak. She held him down with a hand on his chest.

'Soon you can go. The Woodlander cures are strong. They brought you back from the edge of death. Another day, two days, and you can get up. But not yet.'

'I've been here – how long?'

'Six days. Seven nights.'

He was appalled. What had happened to Susan in such

42

a time? 'They were only going to keep her until they thought they were safe.'

'We know. You spoke. Sleep a little while. Perhaps . . .'

She slipped the spoon between his lips and darkness filled him like a liquid rising, and with it came a sense of peace that was — wrong, wrong. Susan was not safe . . . But he let that go, he had to, and he slept, and when he woke Soona was by his bed, and Silverwing the Birdwoman stood like coloured paper, an origami giant, at the foot.

'Silverwing. Have you . . .?'

'Not yet, Nick. But the search goes on.'

'Are you looking in the right place? North?'

'We're looking everywhere. Mountain, forest, swamp. Land and sea.'

'In the Hotlands?'

'As far as we can fly.'

'What did Soona mean, she was there, then was gone?'

'It was four days ago. One of our searching parties in the north, where the sands turn red — they saw men and women, and a girl, a captive, roped. It was Susan.'

'She was alive?'

'Alive. When they flew low the guards held a knife at her throat. So there was nothing they could do. Yellowclaw and I flew to join them. We pleaded, we bargained. We offered riches, power. But they held us at bowshot and made no answer. Their leader cried to us, "Vermin, stay off or she dies." Then, no more. We kept them in sight. But they turned off the sands into the jungle, into valleys, and night came. So we lost them. And no searching has uncovered them. It is a place where nature and creation have gone mad. Jungles, swamps, lakes that boil, chasms that spout steam. And sands, and lava, hills that melt before you, hills that grow overnight and vanish in a day. Whole armies could hide there.'

'They won't need her any more.'

'There are other sands to cross. They fear us, Nick. They will keep her.'

'Was she – did she seem all right?' It was a foolish question. He writhed in the bed, and Soona placed her hand on his shoulder to keep him still. 'They called to her, Nick. Yellowclaw called.'

'Yellowclaw told her you were alive,' Silverwing said. 'He cried out that you had escaped. Then the leader, the tall one, beat a woman, kicked her – she, I suppose, who hunted you. Our eyes are sharp. We can see beetles on stone from mountain height. Tears ran on Susan's face.'

Great, great, Nick thought. Everyone's crying, no one's saving her. But he could think of nothing he might do. 'Are humans searching as well as Birdfolk?'

'Yes,' Soona said. 'My father has sent as many as he can spare.'

'Kenno?'

'He is Chief Minister. He has sent a party of a dozen men, but it will be days yet before they reach the place where she was seen.'

'A dozen? Is that all?'

A blush of shame rose on Soona's cheeks. 'There are many things to do. Bands of roving priests to hunt. The army to organize. Roads to build. Temples to pull down. And men, administrators, to send out all over the land. They must have escorts. And so . . .'

'Susan comes second.'

Soona raised her eyes. 'Yes. With my father. Don't blame him. He has a land to run. He works all the day and half the night. There is so much to do. But with me she is not second, she is first.'

'And with the Birdfolk,' Silverwing said.

'Has someone sent for Jimmy?'

'He and Ben the Varg came back and joined the search. They are with Yellowclaw in the north.'

'I want to see Jimmy. I want to join them.'

'Soon,' Silverwing said. 'When you are stronger. Birdfolk will carry you in a nest.'

Nick turned to Soona. 'When can I go?'

'You nearly died, Nick. Don't be impatient.'

'You should have died,' Silverwing said. 'Cuts and bruises all over you. And burning with fever. Babbling nonsense.'

'Where was I?'

'By a gorge on a river. Someone had lit a fire on the other side, but it was cold. Two days cold.'

'I lay that long? Two days?'

'And would have died there but for your signalling.'

'I signalled?'

'Bird Warriors flying by the seashore saw a light flashing far inland. On and off it went in the setting sun, a tiny light. They flew to it – Birdfolk are curious – and found a boy sitting on a cliff. Half-naked, he was, and feverish, and burned by sun, and croaking, "Water." But in his hands he held a knife – a priest knife with a polished blade – and he turned it to the sun, on and off, calling for help.'

'I dreamed of flashing lights,' Nick said.

'They tended you and put you in a nest and brought you here, and Soona nursed you with her Woodlander skills. We listened to your babble and learned of Susan – '

'And Osro?'

'Who?'

'Did I tell you about their leader?'

'You spoke of renegade priests in the cave, and travelling north, and riding on a river. And danger to Susan. Only that.'

Nick sat up in the bed. 'I've got to see Kenno.'

Soona tried to push him down. 'You're not well enough.'

'You don't know who their leader is. He says he's king. He's worse than the High Priest. He's worse than Otis Claw. He's got a Weapon . . .' He got out of bed and tried to stand, but nearly fell. His head seemed to roll like a melon, heavily. He sat down. 'Please, I've got to tell Kenno.'

'I'll bring him,' Silverwing said. She went from the room, and Soona made him lie and covered him. His head was rolling still, into corners, bruising on walls. He felt a spoon slipped into his mouth; and dimly he saw Soona place something to her own lips and move her fingers on it. Music, flute-notes. Darkness rose again. He slept.

When he woke, sharp familiar eyes were peering at him.

'Limpy,' he said. But was it Limpy? Anxiety was gone from that face and the gleam on it was confident and strict.

'You don't look very well, Nicholas Quinn.'

'I'm O.K. Where's your father? I've got to talk to him.'

'Oh? Get him. Like that? I don't take orders, Nick. I'm more than Limpy the fisherboy now.'

Nick looked at him more closely and saw his eagerness to be important. 'I thought we were friends.'

'Perhaps. But I have work. I am busy now.'

'What do you do?'

'I am assistant to the Chief Minister. His counsellor.'

'You should be out sailing on a boat. You loved the sea.'

'That was when I was a boy. Now I am a man. I help rule the land. So tell me your message. I'll give it to my father if he needs to know.'

There was something sad about him, this fisherboy playing counsellor. Nick spoke less sharply than he wanted to. 'I know a man who calls himself king. Tell you father that. Tell him he's got a Weapon that'll knock your armies flat.'

'What? What's this?'

'Just go and do it.'

46

'Go boy. Do as he says,' Silverwing cried.

Limpy looked angrily at her, but Soona came and pulled him away from the bed. 'Limpy, go. Please. Tell our father. Nick doesn't tell lies.'

Limpy freed his arm. 'You listen too much to people who do not belong on O.' He turned to Nick. 'I'll take your message. But don't try to be my friend. I have better friends.' He went out, trailing his bad leg.

Soona sat on the bed and felt Nick's forehead. 'You are hot. He has made you angry. Don't blame him, Nick. People laughed at him because he limped, and put him to tasks he felt unworthy. But he is brave. And clever. He went to Earth and brought Susan back. And now he is important. My father listens to him.'

'Is your father so important?'

Soona looked troubled. 'He has been chosen Chief Minister. It does not make him happy.'

Silverwing came from the door. 'This man who calls himself king? Who is he?'

'Wait till Kenno comes,' Nick said. 'I don't want to tell it twice. Soona, will you play your flute again?'

The music calmed him, made him think of old times, of floating on the sea, and walking at night. Later in the morning, Kenno came. Nick had hardly known him, and scarcely recognized the blunt and grizzled fisherman in this anxious busy visitor. Yet he was kind, Nick saw it. He sat on the bed and asked his daughter how the patient was, and listened when she answered. Then he said, 'I'm sorry O has captured you again. Our world has been unkind to you and Susan, Nicholas Quinn.'

'It's not your fault. As soon as I can get up I want to look for her.'

'Of course. And I promise you, any who have harmed her will be punished.'

'I don't want revenge. I just want to take Susan home.'

'Yes. I'll help. But I can't stay now. There is so much to do governing O. Tell me about this man who calls himself king. There are many such – kings, emperors, saviours, wizards, madmen. The times breed them. But the people rule. The Council rules. And we must stop these evils before they spread.'

'This one's special. He's got a Weapon.'

'What weapon? Who is he? The Birdfolk said some renegade, some ragged criminal.'

'Not him. He was a Candidate.'

'They're dead. All dead.'

'Not Osro.'

Soona started. She gave a cry. 'He was the mad one. He hummed tunes all the time and dribbled on his chin. But – '

'Yes?' Kenno said.

'His eyes were cunning. He seemed to be enjoying it.'

'He was pretending,' Nick said. 'It was his way of staying alive. And he was plotting. He was going to murder the High Priest and take over.'

'Impossible,' Kenno said. He turned to Limpy at the door. 'What happened to him?'

'We did not bother to hunt him. He was mad. He still is mad, to call himself king.'

'His followers believe him. They'd die for him,' Nick said.

Limpy laughed. 'All ten of them.'

'Still, we must know of it,' Kenno said. 'And his Weapon. What is it, Nick? Some bow that carries further? Some blade that cuts more deeply? We can make those, too.'

'Fire,' Nick said.

'Fire?'

'Some sort of ray. Or flame-thrower. He said it would burn your armies like a field of corn.'

'Crazy talk.'

'They have them on Earth.'

'Earth is not O. Fire is not thrown, or shot into the air like an arrow. The man is mad.'

'Father,' Soona said, 'in the old tales, in the songs, they speak of vapours, minerals, that throw out flames when they are brought together. And feed on men like beasts.'

'Rhymers' nonsense. Stuff for the heads of women.'

Silverwing stepped forward. 'Perhaps,' she said.'But in our ancient books there's talk of such. Conjunctions of stone that flare like the sun. It is hidden in symbol and mystery. Forbidden knowledge.'

Kenno stirred impatiently. 'This wastes my time. Nick, did Osro say where he would go?'

'To the Hotlands.'

'Why?'

'To raise an army. He said the tribes would follow him. They had a treaty.'

'The Hotland tribes are savages. They eat human flesh,' Limpy cried.

'They shave their bodies bare and paint themselves bright blue and brighter red. They worship sticks and stones,' Kenno said. 'Gods in mountains, gods in the trees.'

Soona had gone pale. 'But most they worship fire,' she said. 'Their great god is fire.' She held them silent as she looked at them. 'And Osro brings it. Fire to burn up armies. To burn O.'

Kenno was the first to recover. 'You listen to the Woodlanders too much. It turns your head. Osro is a madman. He has some toy that spits out flame – if he has that. Our armies will crush these savages he brings. Crush him, too. Limpy, come. Nick, get well. Find Susan and take her home to Earth. There is no more you can do on O.' He started for the door.

'Wait,' Nick said. Kenno stopped. 'Osro had a paper with his calculations on it. Equations and so on.'

'For his Weapon?'

'Yes. He was doing them again. That means he must have done them before. And done experiments.'

'You think we should search his room? The whole Temple was searched. Nothing was found.'

'Do it again. Pull up the floor. Break down the walls. There's got to be something.'

Kenno sighed. 'I will put men to it. But it wastes my time.' He rubbed his face tiredly. 'Come and see me before you go. And see our Council Hall. Now I must go. We must prepare to crush this new king, Osro.' He and Limpy left, and for a time no one spoke. Then Soona said, 'He's so tired.'

'He does too much,' Silverwing said.

'I wish we were still fisherfolk in Stonehaven.'

They left Nick to rest, and came for him in the evening, and they walked in one of the gardens of the old temple. Statues of High Priests, and of Susan, lay overturned and broken in corners. Nick found one of himself drowned in a fountain, with marble legs poking at the sky. The best place for it, he thought, but wished he could have seen it standing up. He thought he was better-looking than the face that frowned up at him through water. He turned away and said to Soona, 'Did they search Osro's room?'

'Yes. They found a secret cell beyond the wall. But Limpy will not say what was in it. He tells me to play music and not worry about important things.'

Nick grunted angrily. Limpy would probably say the same to Susan, in spite of all the things she had done. He found himself caring less and less about O. There were just a few people he cared about, people or beings – Jimmy and Ben, Silverwing and Yellowclaw, Dawn. And Soona too. And Susan. What he had to concentrate on was finding

50

her and getting her back home. Osro and his weapon were no worry of his. He looked at a statue of Susan standing in a niche in a wall. Someone had knocked the head off and it lay like a football at her feet. Next to it was a larger niche, with Jimmy standing in it, unbroken, and so life-like he seemed about to say something. He spoke.

'Gidday, youngker. Yer lookin' skinny on it. Not eatin' yer greens?'

It was not a niche. A door. And it was Jimmy. He stepped into the garden, and Ben the Varg, huge, blue, rippling in the light, shambled after him, with shoulders brushing the frame on either side.

'Jimmy,' Nick cried, running forward. The old man grinned and shook him by his arms, and Ben gave him a friendly butt that almost sent him tumbling into the fountain.

'Jimmy, they told me you were up in the Hotlands. Have you found her? Where is she?'

'No, we ain't,' Jimmy growled. He sat down on the fountain rim. 'No sign of her. This bloddy land won't leave her alone. It's gunner wring out every drop she's got.'

'Did you see the Birdfolk? Are they still looking?'

'I seen that Yellowclaw. He's comin' back.' He looked at Silverwing. 'Be here in the mornin'. He's just organizin' Birdfolk ter watch this army gettin' mobilized up in the north. Geezers what paints themselves. Ther's some bloddy talk they got a king an' they're headin' south. They're gunner stick our heads up on poles. There's Birdfolk tellin' Kenno about it now. It's a bloddy shambles. All I want ter do is get back south.'

'You can't,' Nick cried. 'There's Susan.'

'Yeah, I ain't fergotten.'

'Was she there? With the army? With the king?'

51

'No, she weren't. No one's seen 'er. Not since that time on the sand.'

'Then . . .'

'No,' Jimmy said sharply. 'She ain't dead. I dunno where she is but she ain't dead.'

'How do you know?'

'Because of Ben. He ain't felt it.'

Nick looked at the bear drinking placidly from the fountain. He lifted his head and looked at Nick and suddenly Susan was there, in his mind – Susan alive. His knees went weak with relief. He sat down beside Jimmy.

'He don't know where she is, Nick. He can't tell. She's a big country. She's a bloddy nightmare. Makes Rotorua look like a Turkish bath. Steam an' boilin' pools an' lakes of mud. Lava runnin' like tomato soup. An' sand, hot sand, fries yer like an egg. Ole Ben, he likes the ice. He couldn' take it. Bloddy near pegged out. So we come back. But he knows she ain't snuffed it. He would've felt. Like a kind've needle going in. That's what it's like when someone dies that they're friendly with.'

'Then where is she?'

'Wish I knew. But I reckon she's out of them Hotlands. It's swarming with them geezers now, painted red an' blue. They'd have her if she was there, head on a pole. Ole Ben, he reckons we should look down by the coast. Reckon 'e wants ter catch a fish or two, the cunnin' ole bogger.'

'Let's go then. Let's go now.'

'In the mornin', eh. We gotter rest. And Dawn's on 'er way.'

'Dawn?'

'She went down south. Teamed up with 'er mate. They're comin' back. Be here termorrer. Ben can tell. Now I gotter get some shuteye, Nick. Been walkin' five days straight. Me feet's all swollen up like Christmas puddin's.'

'I'll find you a room in the tower,' Soona said. 'What about Ben?'

'He can doss down here. Might catch some goldfish in them pools, eh ole feller?'

When Nick passed Jimmy's door on his way to bed the old man was snoring like a sawmill. In the morning Limpy came and took them to the Council Hall. Yellowclaw had arrived and made his report, but Dawn and her Varg were out in Wildwood. The bear was shy of humans, Jimmy said, and would not come in.

'We'll team up with them later on today when we take orf.'

'Are we going today?'

'No use wastin' time. You fit enough?'

'I could run a marathon,' Nick said.

Yellowclaw came and gave him a friendly pat with one of his wings. 'You're thinner, Nick. And you have scars. And harder now. And older. That is plain. You have grown up fast.'

'No news of Susan?'

'None. She's not with this Osro and his army, we're sure of that. But Silverwing and I will search with you. There's no more we can do for Kenno.'

'Is Osro's army big?'

'The tribes are massing. Men so fierce and so in love with killing they remind me of Bloodcats. Women too, with spears and clubs and axes. And babies strapped on their backs. There are thousands of them. How this Osro bends them to his will we do not know. Kenno's army will need all its courage. And there is talk of a Weapon — some new thing that shoots fire at the sky.'

'That's how Osro holds them, with fire.'

'Birds cannot fight it. This will be a battle fought by humans.'

Nick looked at Kenno. He sat in a raised chair at one end of a huge oval table. Around were thirty or thirty-five men, no women. They were merchants and shopkeepers of the town, Nick supposed; and several were ex-priests, for they raised their hands by habit to where Ferris bones had hung from their necks. They were soft men, or withered; quick and cunning men of property, who would naturally find places on this — what was it called? — interim council. Alongside them, Kenno the fisherman was brown and weatherbeaten, slow and strong — and confused. Nick saw how he turned his head as if he wondered how he had come here. And then he blinked, and set his mouth. When he spoke the others inclined their heads, agreed with him, but Nick had the feeling he spoke words they chose. They talked of conscripting men, appointing generals, arming regiments. Of contracts for this and that. 'Yes, yes,' Kenno said, 'as long as we are ready. The details of payment I leave to you.'

'Why is his chair higher than the others?' Nick whispered.

'They voted it to him. He did not want it,' Soona said.

'They'll vote him emperor next,' Jimmy growled. Nick said nothing, but agreed. He did not think the common people would vote. Somehow the times would never be right for elections. Kenno would be king or emperor, or maybe just president for life. These men would manage him and he would not know. And then, when his usefulness was done, someone would organize a coup. And they would execute the 'tyrants'. Perhaps they would throw them off Sheercliff. Kenno and poor Limpy. Soona too . . .

His reverie was broken by a noise at the door. A man hurried in, waving a piece of paper, and ran round the table to Kenno's chair. Kenno looked at the paper, then handed it to the secretary beside him. Of course, Nick thought, he can't read. That must be handy for the ones who managed him. The secretary — a hungry-looking ex-priest — scanned the paper. His eyes gleamed. He whispered to Kenno and they conferred with the man who had come in. Then Kenno said, 'Council members, our scientists have uncovered the secret of Osro's Weapon. Here is their report. It is hard to understand, but I will ask the Chief Scientist to tell it simply.' He had a chair brought and the man sat down and began to talk. His excitement infected everyone at the table.

'Men of O, it is this. Osro had a store of ancient books and there he found the pathway to his Weapon. Whatever his faults, he was a great man. Years he must have studied, hidden behind the false wall in his cell. His calculations — the intricacy of them. And his apparatus, experiments, they take the breath away — '

'Enough of this,' cried a fat man halfway round the table. 'Speak of the Weapon. Can you make it?'

'Yes. I have a team. They are working now. The mechanics are difficult. But, six days, seven, it will be done. And the materials. I have sent men out. There are deposits south along the coast, and inland, in the mountains, at the back of the Throat of the Underworld. Osro had the places marked. And trees are being tapped for oils. All is under way.'

'What does it do, this Weapon?'

The Chief Scientist sighed. He raised his glowing eyes. 'Marvels of destruction.'

'Be precise.'

'We make a construction of multiple chambers. And place in each an ingredient. Metal. Vapour. Oil. And bring them together — with great care. With absolute precision. And contain their meeting, and direct their force . . .'

'Force?'

55

'A beam. A beam of — something. Light or fire, we do not know.'

'What does it do?'

The man drew in his breath. 'What does it not do? It will burn trees and melt stone. And shrivel men to ashes, more quickly than that.' He snapped his fingers. 'It will make lakes boil. It will sear down buildings, wood or brick or marble, it matters not.'

'How wide is the beam?'

'It can be widened or narrowed. Made stronger or weaker. That is simple.'

'The range?'

'With it I can melt the tops of the mountains beyond Wildwood.'

'Ha!' cried the fat man excitedly.

'But Osro has the Weapon,' Kenno said.

'Then we must have more and better ones,' the fat man said. 'And strike before he is ready. Then we can go further north. The tribes there are even more primitive than the Hotlanders. It will be our mission to conquer and civilize them. And then, the riches, the trade.'

'Hold!' Kenno said. 'We will have no talk of conquest. Our war against Osro is defensive.'

'And you mustn't make these weapons,' Nick cried. 'You must capture Osro before he can use his.'

'Who is this boy?' the fat man said.

'By what right does he speak?' another asked.

'Father,' Soona called out, 'Nick is right. Please don't make it. The old tales say it consumes its maker.'

'And it is forbidden to Birdfolk,' Yellowclaw said. 'The Weapon is evil. We can have no part in this war.'

'Would you have us sit here while Osro conquers us?' Kenno said.

56

'Capture him. Before he makes his Weapon. We will help in that.'

'It is made already. He knew the way,' the scientist cried.

'Then Birdfolk must withdraw from your battle.'

'Withdraw from our Council Hall too,' the fat man said. 'Withdraw over your mountains. We do not need you. We have the Weapon.'

'Hold!' Kenno cried. 'Silence!' When all was quiet, he turned sadly to Nick and Jimmy and the Birdfolk. 'We thank you for your help. But our ways must part. We must fight this war, and fight with the Weapon. That is clear. Osro must not rule. He would want the whole of O. No one would be safe. So we must stop him. But Birdfolk and Woodlanders and Varg are safe from us. All the Folk. We seek no conquest.' He believed it, Nick saw, and he felt overwhelmed with sorrow for Kenno. 'Now you must go and seek your friend and take her back to Earth. And we must go on with our counsels. That is the way of it. So – goodbye.'

'Father,' Soona said, 'I will go with them. Susan is my friend.'

'As you choose, my daughter. Come back safely. If all goes well we will know peace then.'

They turned and left the chamber, left Kenno and his Councilmen talking of the Weapon, and banded together at the Temple gates. Limpy came to say goodbye. Now that they were leaving, he seemed to regret his sharp words to Nick. They shook hands.

'Don't worry,' Limpy said, 'we'll beat Osro.'

'Look after your father. He needs help,' Nick replied.

Limpy did not understand. He embraced his sister and stood waving at the gate, a lopsided figure, until their path took them into the forest.

Dawn and her Varg were waiting there. The sight of the

Woodlander girl lifted Nick's spirits: her downy, coloured face, her laugh, her quickness. The bears nuzzled each other. Over the trees, Silverwing and Yellowclaw called greetings.

'Which way shall we go, Jimmy?' Nick said.

'North up through the mountains. Then down to the coast. I'm not going near them Hotlands. Makes me feel like bacon in a pan.'

'That's a long way.'

'We gotter start somewhere. It ain't gunner be easy, Nick. She's a big country.'

'I know. Are you ready, Soona?'

She was standing apart, looking at her flute. She raised it and blew notes, soft and dark. They echoed in the trees. He frowned at her. 'Come on. There's no time for music.'

She smiled. 'Nick,' she said, 'there's someone we should ask.'

'What about?'

'Susan. Can you find a cave for me? One that goes deep into the hills.'

The Hotlands

For the first time in their five-day march Susan felt more than a thing of rags, led on a string. She felt her heart beating. Tears ran on her cheeks and dripped as hot as candle wax on her arms. Osro had knocked Slarda down and was kicking her. She heard the woman squeal and Osro grunt. It did not matter. They were puppets now, rags and bone. Nick was alive, he was not dead. If that was true (and it was true, for Yellowclaw had said it) Osro could be beaten. For five days she had trodden numbly, expecting her death. She was not afraid now.

Yellowclaw and the Birdfolk turned in the sky, out of bowshot. She knew how sharp their eyes were, and she smiled at them, said, 'Thank you.' They would see.

'Master,' Slarda cried, 'you are killing me.'

Osro kicked again. 'The boy was dead. You told me. You lied.'

'No, Master. We heard our bolts strike home. We saw him fall. Greely and I.'

Osro swung to the girl, trembling nearby.

'Saw him. Pierced him with our bolts,' she cried. 'We heard his body fall in the river.'

Osro struck her face flat-handed. 'I am cursed with fools. The boy tricked you.'

'The Birds are lying, Master.'

'They don't lie.'

Slarda said, 'Does it matter? He can do no harm.'

'I spoke to him of the Weapon. He will tell this Council of Freemen. They will make their own.'

'Master, it is difficult – '

'It is not. The work is done, written down for them to find.'

'Perhaps he will not speak. He will forget.'

'Perhaps! There is no perhaps. We must raise our army. Strike before they are ready. And we must lose these sky-borne vermin now. Get up. Bring the girl. She is useful yet.'

He turned across the red dunes towards the rim of jungle. It shimmered in a haze. The sand was the colour of rusty iron. Heat rose from it, throbbing. They walked through ponds of heat. Susan felt if she did not keep her head up she would drown. Steen walked behind, holding her rope. A change had come on Steen since Nick had crushed the Shy in his face. He rarely spoke. He watched Susan with strange puzzled eyes. For two days he had ridden in a litter. Then he walked again, but not as guide. He had lost his hardness, seemed to dream and wonder. The others no longer spoke to him. Slarda took his crossbow. He was useful only as Susan's guard. She welcomed his turn on her rope. He let it hang more loosely than the others. And sometimes, when they paused on the burning sand, he stood so his shadow fell on her and eased the sun.

The Birdfolk were specks. As the day went on she lost any sense that they were real. They were tiny things suspended in a pool. They were specks swimming in her eye. The jungle rose. It was black and green, full of openings where creepers hung like fly-stops in doorways. Blood-red flowers lay in the darkness, beating, pulsing. She stepped into the shade. It was warm and wet. She felt as if she had gone inside an animal's body. The desert was its skin. This was mouth and gullet. She was swallowed.

Steen nudged her on. They went down, climbing, sliding, deep into a gully where everything that grew was black or brown and grown too large. Leaves like rubber doormats, limp and fat. Flowers with black trumpets and black tongues, opening wider than an oil drum and giving out a stink like ensilage. She looked up. The sky was gone.

'They cannot see us,' Osro said. 'But somewhere we must cross the sands again. Then the tribes will find us and Birds trouble us no more.'

And, Susan thought, they won't need me. Insects as large as sparrows were droning up from the gully bed. They made a dancing iridescent flash. One of the women cried with pain. Quietly, unseen, Steen unrolled his blanket and covered Susan's head.

'Master, we must climb out of here,' Slarda said. 'These bloodsuckers are too many to fight.'

'Keep on a while. We must strike in deep.'

They went down the gully in a whirl and hum of insects. Somewhere on the higher plains a beast was roaring like a Jersey bull. Slarda armed her bow. The gully ended in a swamp where trees grew knee-deep in water red as plum juice. Bubbles rose in it and sat on the surface. Susan wondered if they were eyes, but they burst with a sticky pop and new ones oozed up to replace them. Something was stirring deep down in the water. She knew if she escaped she would not live long in this jungle.

They climbed into a drier place and the insects fell away. The jungle opened out, with taller trees, and colours more like those of Earth. Susan felt it was like the bush around her home. There were creepers like supple-jack, and others that grabbed like bush lawyer. Ferns grew in the under-storey, and tiny birds looped and darted, catching gnats. Somewhere high, another sang like a tui. Osro led them on for several hours, and Susan knew that if she got away she would have a chance here. There were even fruits she recognized from Wildwood. Steen picked one and gave it to her to eat.

Towards dark they came to broken hills and criss-crossed gullies. Steam rose from hollows in the ground and once shot hissing from a mouth-shaped hole in the side of a hill. She had guessed they were coming to this, for the jungle had been wrapped in a rotten-egg smell for some time. They crossed a little creek where the water ran warm. She hoped that tonight she would be able to wash her face and hands in a hot pool.

Osro stopped and the guards made camp. Slarda and Greely went off to hunt and came back with the carcase of an animal like a pig. They boiled pieces of it in a pool that bubbled in a cluster of stones. Osro had gone into his shelter. He ate alone. Steen brought Susan meat and fruit, and later let her wash with the women guards in a deep warm basin above the camp. She slept almost comfortably that night. No chance came for escape, but she consoled herself with the knowledge that Nick was alive and free.

For two more days they travelled north. At times the steam was so dense the jungle seemed on fire. Mud lakes boiled like porridge pots. Cliffs steamed and geysers burst from mounds and roared in jets and sprays and feathers high into the air. Around them the bush was warped and mineral-crusted. The trunks of trees gleamed white and pink and blue.

They cooked pig-meat and deer-meat, and caught crayfish in cold pools and boiled them in hot. Susan felt almost too well-fed. But she watched everything. She might have to survive alone in this place.

On the third night Slarda said, 'Master, tomorrow we will reach the sands again and we must cross.'

'We have the girl. And we can cross at night if we need. There is no danger.'

'Then,' Slarda said, 'let us rid ourselves of her. She slows our march.'

'Keep her, keep her,' Osro said. 'You can have her soon.'
He had eaten with them, not in his shelter. He was pleased
with himself that night. 'Earth-girl, you have travelled with
the ruler of O. But you do not seem to know who I am.'

'Oh, I know,' Susan said. 'We have your sort. You're like
Adolf Hitler or Al Capone. You're a gangster.'

'Who are these? Great men? What is a gangster?'

'Why don't you marry Slarda? She'd be a good queen.'

'Master,' Slarda cried, 'let me silence her.'

'No, no,' Osro said. 'She presumes. But she is harmless.
She speaks so to keep her courage up. It interests me. I shall
be king, Susan Ferris, not just because I have the Weapon
and lead the tribes but because I know how people think
— how their minds go, how they move, from here, to here,
to here.' He made little movements with his hands. 'It is
all so tiny and pathetic, and to one who sits above it all
and sees, predictable. I can turn them, and place them, these
small ones, so — and so. Therefore, I am king. I am greater.'

'Perhaps,' Susan said. She had the sick feeling it might be
true. 'But in the end you'll die, like everyone else. And be
forgotten.'

Osro's eyes flashed, and narrowed briefly. Then he
laughed. 'That is true. I don't forget. But before that happens,
how wide I shall spread myself, how great I shall grow. And
the games I shall have with my little toys.'

'People won't let you. They won't follow.'

'Oh, but they will. Already they do. So eagerly. They
cannot wait to give themselves away. They think they are
part of me. Is it not so, Slarda?'

'Yes, Master.' She did not understand, but her eyes shone
with devotion as she looked at him and her horsey teeth
turned pink in the firelight.

'You see, Susan? But first, of course, there is the war to
fight. I shall bring fire to the tribes. My Weapon. They

worship fire, and they shall worship me. I shall lead them against these Freemen and strike before they are ready. And burn them into ashes. They will join me, those who are left, they will be mine, part of me. And I shall give them enemies, creatures to hate. Birdfolk and Woodlanders and Varg. And lead them to conquer new lands. They shall shout with one voice and think, if at all, with one mind – which I control. That is the new history of O, Susan Ferris. You played your little part in the old, but you have no part written in the new.'

She could not answer. She felt very tired, and told herself that tomorrow, chance or not, she would escape. Osro turned away and went into his shelter, but the memory of his face, with its sharp bones and hungry mouth and pale hot eyes, stayed with her as she tried to sleep. Steen threw a blanket over her and sat behind her on a stone, holding the rope knotted round her waist. The embers in the fire dulled.

She did not know she had slept, but knew she was woken. She was cold, the blanket gone. And someone was kneeling by her head. She heard the gristly creaking of his spine as he bent close. Fingers nipped her mouth so she could not scream.

'No sound. If they wake we are dead.' It was Steen. 'Follow the rope. Go where it leads.'

She heard him stand, and knew she had no choice but to follow. With no one to trust, she would trust him. She sat up, stood up, felt the rope tugging at her waist. She stepped after it, past the pale blur of Osro's shelter. She had no idea where the guards were sleeping, but heard snorts and gurgles, whispered dreams, nightmare slayings. Steen took her soft-footed round their edge. She heard the exhalations of his breath. A hot pool hissed and simmered as they passed – heading west, or starting west. The jungle made a humming; distant screams as something died. Steen led her into it, giving little tugs like a fisherman feeling bites.

'Steen.'

'Don't speak. Not yet.'

She followed, walking blind, for what seemed hours. At last he stopped. She felt his fingers working on the knots and the rope fell away. He put the end in her hand. 'Hold it now and follow.'

'Why are you doing this? Helping me?'

For a moment he made no answer. She seemed to see his eyes moving faintly in the dark. 'I can be this Osro's man no longer. So I will take you to your friends.'

'They'll kill you if they catch you.'

'They'll kill us both. We must get far away. They will hunt, but not for long. Osro cannot waste the time.'

'Slarda won't give up.'

'She is the one. We must keep ahead. Do you have the rope?'

She gave it a jerk.

'Hold and follow.'

'What about animals?'

'We must take the risk.'

She could not tell how long they went on then, but guessed three or four hours. They climbed spurs and threaded through valleys, crossing streams that were cold or warm, and sometimes both. Steen seemed to know his way; but told her when she asked that he did not know this part of the jungle, he was heading west, that was all.

'Why west?'

'We'll go to the coast. Birdfolk will find you there. Or perhaps these Seafolk men say you talk with.'

'I can talk with them. And Stonefolk. And Woodlanders. Varg too, in a way.'

'I know nothing. That is all I know.'

Dawn came, lighting the sky, but leaving the jungle almost as dark as night. Steen gave her meat from his pack. They found berries, sour but edible, and drank from a spring tasting of iron. It set her teeth on edge.

'Do you need to rest?'

'I can keep going.'

'They have woken and found us gone. Slarda hunts. She tracks like a dog. We must stay ahead.'

She tried to see his face but could make out only his eyes, pale and gleaming, and the movements of his hands as he carried food to his mouth. A few days ago he had wanted to kill her. Now he risked his life to help her escape.

'Why can't you follow Osro?'

'I don't know. I cannot. Something in me says, turn away.'

'Because he's evil?'

'I don't know evil. I don't know good. I know nothing.'

'Was it the Shy?'

'The stinkweed? When the boy crushed it in my face, then I seemed to lose all I knew. But for a moment there was something. It said no, and it said yes. To one way and another. But I can't — I can't remember. And I must. Something goes before me, but it turns, it eludes me, I glimpse it but it will not stay and let itself be seen. All it tells me now is — I am alone. And so I must not be Osro's man.'

'What will you do? When we're safe?'

'I'll go into the mountains. Live alone. And find there the thing that I must know.'

'You can use the Shy again.'

'Perhaps. I would sooner learn it for myself.'

'You'd have a better chance of getting away if you left me.'

'I cannot.'

They started west again, the sun behind them. It slanted through the trees and brought some light to the jungle floor.

Then the jungle shrank, and soon they pushed through scrub that pricked like gorse. Steam rose ahead, with cliffs and towers that seemed to be trekking by like misshapen men.

'We are at the Belt,' Steen said. 'A place gone mad. It rots the land like gangrene. O burns in a fever here.'

'Do we have to go in?'

'It runs north and south. So we cross. One day, one night. Then more sands. Iron, pumice, copper. Beyond that jungle, down to the sea.'

'Can't we find the Birdfolk?'

'I've looked. They're searching elsewhere.'

'Steen – '

'Don't be afraid. Test every step. We'll use the rope.' He tied an end round her waist and knotted the other in his belt. They walked over pumice sand, through fissures wet by steam and dried by heat. The bushes dwindled, giving way to scurfy weed and rock in clusters. Then they were in the cliffs and towers, which leaned away from them or bent over. They were like giants peering to see or jerking back. The steam turned and surged like blown cloud. It wet their faces and their clothes. Water covered them like sweat, dripping from their chins and fingertips. At least Slarda can't track us here, Susan thought. She followed Steen's back. She trusted him. He was almost as broad as he was tall – built like a barn door, Nick would say. She trusted him to find a way through this.

They went round the side of a boiling spring half as long as a football field, and followed the river flowing out. It churned through rapids, dived over falls, but did not lose its heat until it joined a cold stream flowing from the south. Steam sprang up from their meeting, rolling in the monoliths and blotting out the sky. They crossed further down, swimming roped together in water warm as tea.

By night they had climbed out of wet into dry. They slept on shaly stone warmed from underground and Susan had nightmares as though covered with too many blankets. She felt a stirring as if the hill she slept on was shifting. In the morning she saw they were on the inner slope of a huge pit.

'Here a mountain was swallowed,' Steen said. 'O is hollow underneath and feeds on herself. And spits herself out.' A rumbling came from the west. 'That is her sound. She has no manners.' He smiled – the first smile she had seen from him. It lit his heavy face and seemed to give a lighter colour to his slaty eyes. 'We should reach the sands by afternoon.'

They went round the pit and crossed a trembling plain and climbed the flank of a long low mountain stretching north. Lava wormed from holes blown in its sides. It crumbled as it nosed down the slope. Smoking stones rolled on ahead. The mountain itself was lava-built. Great flat tongues lay on the landscape south.

It took them all day to get across. By nightfall they were in the scrub. Steen wrapped blankets round them to save them from the thorns. He kept on to the edge of a dry-grass plain, where he gave Susan meat and fruit and water.

'The sands are close. We will not stop but go straight across. Slarda cannot be far away. She will hope to pick up our trail on the sand. But when we reach the jungle I can lose her.'

'How long will we be on the sands?'

'All night and all the morning. Perhaps we'll sleep an hour, we'll see. Before the hottest sun we'll reach the jungle.'

That did not seem bad. It was no great desert. And though she was tired she would rather keep going if Slarda was close.

The night was black. She followed the rope. Soon they left the grass and climbed in dunes. Steen had some way of finding firm-packed sand and she found the walking easy at first. In places a brittle grass still grew. It pricked her legs. Later it was gone and the sand was finer, shifting and sliding. She felt as if she were trudging in mud. It grew harder to lift her feet. Steen let her rest twice but would not let her sleep. He kept a tension on the rope and she felt as if she were a broken car being towed along.

At last he said, 'Midnight. Sleep a while.'

'Can I have some water?'

He gave her his flask.

'Have we got enough?'

'There's a water-hole halfway across. We should find it at sunrise.'

She drank, and covered herself with a blanket. When he woke her she thought no more than a moment had passed. But he said, 'Morning in two hours. We must get close to the water-hole. Slarda will find our trail. She will be fresh and we are tired.' He led her among dunes cresting like breakers. Then he found a plain of hard flat sand and they walked more easily. Soon she felt dry grass brushing her legs. The sky behind them lightened and he took the rope and looped it in his belt.

'Over the rise. Can you smell water?'

'No.'

'It is the smell of life in the sands.' He moved again, but stopped uncertainly.

'What is it?'

'Ashes. Dead fires.'

'Who?'

'Hotlanders. I hope they've gone.'

He went on until they came to the rise. It was like a bank round a fortified village. Steen put his hand back and stopped her. She saw his eyes gleaming in the dawn-light. 'Stay here.' He climbed, bent at the waist, and crouched below the rim of the bank. She lost hope. If no one was there he would have called. Then he beckoned, putting his fingers to his lips. She crept up to his side and looked where he was pointing, at the oasis. Colours moved about it as if a cloth were rippling on the ground. It took her a moment to understand that people, men and women, naked except for loin-cloths, shaven-headed, painted over their bodies blue and red, were moving in a silent ritual dance about the few black bushes, the yard or so of water.

'They dance to welcome the sun. He is their god, or one of them.'

'The god of fire.'

Blue lines rippled through the red. Clusters, splashes, formed here and there; and suddenly the dance had a burning core, a concentration of red so bright it seemed to throb. The sun came over the bank. A shout rose to greet it, an exultant yell. That was all. The simplicity of it startled Susan. The Hotlanders broke up and moved to their morning tasks. She was able to look at one or two and see them more closely. They were tall and sinewy, with a mantis angularity. Their colours made them beautiful, yet in a way that was frightening. She got from them a sense of threat and savagery, a sense of suddenness. They would, she thought, see and kill, with nothing in between – a single action. They looked as if they could run all day, exist on a mouthful of water. The desert was theirs, they belonged.

Iron age, she thought, looking at their weapons; yet they did not seem that civilized. The women, tall and stringy as the men, were painted blue. They were the axe and club warriors. The men carried whippy spears, red like themselves.

'Is it war paint?'

'No,' Steen said. 'It wards off the sun. They paint themselves differently for war. This must be a band on its way to join Osro.'

'Will they really follow him?'

70

'The Hotlands are theirs. They believe darkness lies outside. But Osro will lead them with his Weapon. Fire and light. They will follow.'

'Will they stay here long – at the water-hole?'

'The men are setting up targets for their spears. They will stay all morning. And Slarda comes behind. So . . .' He shrugged.

'What about water?'

'A mouthful each.' He looked at his flask. 'We must reach the jungle by midday. Otherwise . . .'

They backed down the slope and rounded the water-hole to the south. Soon they crossed the trail left by the Hotlanders and struck out into the dunes. Steen kept them in hollows and when he climbed at last the water-hole was gone and sand was all about like a sea. Susan looked ahead for the jungle but only pale sky showed on the horizon. Later it vanished in a pool of heat. Steen tore head-coverings from his blanket but heat burned through and clung to them, dry and sticky at once. The sand radiated heat, at the same time dragging their feet. Susan felt she was walking up to her knees, but floating too, horizontal, squeezed flat by the pressure from above and below.

'Steen, I need some water.'

'One sip.' He pulled the flask away. 'We're not halfway there.'

They went on. She had a time of clarity and fierceness. She followed Steen, stepping in his steps. If this was the worst then she would do it.

'Steen?'

'Yes?'

'How close?'

'An hour. The jungle. See.'

Something was forming in the heat. It would not stay still. 'It looks alive. It looks like a snake.'

Steen gave her the flask. 'Finish it now.' It made a hollow rattle and was empty before her mouth was wet. Steen let the last drops fall on his palm. He licked them off and fastened the flask on his belt. 'Water in the jungle. Can you get there?'

'I think so.'

Half an hour later she wasn't sure. The dunes had a steep side and a flat side, and the steep always faced them and had to be climbed. Steen began hauling her up like a swimmer from a pool. Then he stood her and pulled her to the next climb. She heard him grunt and pant, and when she managed to look at him his eyes were blind from his exertions. She wondered why he made them go so fast.

'Steen?'

'We must keep moving.' He was using himself up and she saw no need for it. The jungle was close. The glassy wall of heat was lifted away. She saw individual trees, and green round heads printed on the sky.

'Steen?'

'Slarda is coming.'

'Where?' She looked back. Nothing was there, only dune-tops, salty-white. Then a brown speck showed, and swelled from the surface into a questing four-legged shape. She thought it was a dog, but it stood, grew into a stick-limbed man or woman, treading quickly; and shrank again, sank into a hollow between dunes, and went from sight.

'Is it her?'

'Yes. She's closing. I have watched her.'

'Has she seen us?'

'She follows our footmarks. That is her way. We can't get to the jungle, there's no time. Not both of us.'

She stared at him with fear. He was going to leave her. But he shook his head, smiled in his flat-mouthed way. 'I

72

cannot save myself. I don't know why. I must stay and fight. She has her crossbow, so I must hide and ambush her.'

'If she sees you first . . .'

'Then I am dead. It doesn't trouble me. All things die. But I die as Steen, not Osro's man. And not as priest. I thank you for that.'

'Can't we both – '

'No. While I fight with Slarda you must reach the jungle. Wait there, I will find you.' He gave his smile again. 'If it's her – then I'm sorry. Quickly. Go.'

She tried to say thank you but could not make her mouth work. Instead, she touched his hand. Then she turned and left him. She walked down the slope of the dune and reached the face of the next. When she looked back Steen was gone. She climbed the face, using hands and feet, and looked again from the top. Wherever he was, he was hidden well. But Slarda was there, topping another dune two hundred metres back. It was like watching someone over a river. Slarda made no sign of seeing her, but sank into a hollow. For a moment her head seemed to float on the sand, then was gone. Susan ran, stumbling down to another sand-face. This one seemed more steep. She slid back as she climbed. At the top she rolled until she was hidden, then ran again, and climbed; and so it went on, three more, four more, five more dunes. She looked back but had no sight of Slarda. By now the woman must have reached the place where Steen had left her.

A cry came from the desert. It crossed the huge silence like an arrow, and was gone. Male or female? Susan could not tell. She ran across sand that did not fall as she had expected but seemed as flat as a low-tide beach, and came to the final climb. The jungle stood there, silent, at the top of a wall white as sugar. It seemed almost straight up and down and taller by several times than the ones she had climbed already. She started up, and slid back, and knew she had no strength for it. But she tried again, and made several metres, digging her fingers in the moving surface. Far away, black creepers hung like strands of hair on a forehead. If she could reach one — but she fell, and rolled like a log to the bottom. Her eyes were blind with sand and her mouth gritty. She squatted hamster-like at the foot of the wall and waited for whatever was to happen. After a little time her eyes were clear. She wiped them and looked across the sand-flat at the dunes. Slarda stood halfway across, watching her.

Slarda!

Susan thought of Steen first. Tears burned in her eyes and slid on her cheeks. She was glad that he had died his own man. Then she was terrified for herself, and tried to stand, but her knees gave way.

Slarda came another ten steps forward. Her lips were drawn back in a grin, her teeth gleamed like porcelain. She held up something, rattled it — Steen's belt and empty water flask — and threw it aside. She took her crossbow from her back and with two fingers shaped like tongs plucked a short arrow from her pouch.

If only she'd say something, say a word, Susan thought. She could not move. She sat at the foot of the sandhill, leaning her back on it, palms flat, calves burning on the sand, and waited for Slarda to take aim. Grains from high on the hill ran in little rivers by her face. She tried to wet her mouth. She closed her eyes.

When she opened them Slarda had her bow armed. But something about her was wrong. She had sunk into a fighting crouch. She was looking not at Susan but up at the jungle. Slowly she took two steps back.

Susan turned painfully. She did not care much what she saw. It could be no help, whatever it was.

74

The sand climbed almost straight, as smooth as marble. Jungle frothed across the top of it. A huge red flower bloomed on the green. She blinked and looked again. Not a flower. Jaws and shoulders jutting like a painted figurehead. White teeth winking. Eyes like jewels.

Bloodcat!

CHAPTER SIX

Thief

'Cat,' Slarda said, 'take the girl.' Her voice came hoarsely over the sand. 'Cat, noble cat, we are hunters, you and I. We understand each other. She was mine. But I surrender her. I give her to you. Take the girl.'

The Bloodcat made no sign of having heard. It opened its jaws wide and yawned and the bones of its mouth made a creaking sound.

'Cat,' Slarda said, 'she is tender. She is sweet. But I am tough. No meal for you, King of Cats.'

She was pleading for her life. But she made no sign of panic. She remained in her fighting crouch, with her bow ready. Her eyes, unblinking, watched the cat. Susan watched it too, thinking how much less terrible it was than Slarda. It was not twisted, it would not kill her for its own pleasure. And it would do as it wanted. She felt like telling Slarda to stop wasting her time. This cat would choose one of them, or both. And that would be that.

It placed one paw over the lip of sand, testing it. Then it stepped out and slid down, forelegs stiff and tail like a snake. It was so bright on the sand Susan shielded her eyes. She heard the wooden slap of Slarda's bow. The cat twisted, almost lazily, shifting its line, and kept on sliding. The bolt pocked the sand and slid down too, a stocky poisonous dart with a needle tip. Sand buried it at the foot of the slope.

Susan watched the cat. It stepped out on the flat and stretched itself like a house cat at a fire. Again it yawned and its jaws creaked. It seemed lazy, bored, but its tail gave it away, whipping stiffly from side to side. Still it seemed to pay no attention to Slarda; and Susan gave her no attention either. She heard the frantic jacking of her bow as she reloaded. Slarda was a movement at the corner of her eye. The cat filled the rest. It stopped its yawning and turned to face her. She saw those eyes again, that she had seen in nightmares — hot and yellow, pupils in a flame-point. They seemed to cut into her like knives, penetrate to where heart throbbed and lungs pumped. She seemed to have no secrets from the cat, it saw into her brain to where the secret of her life was kept.

'Cat,' Susan whispered, 'don't. Please.'

She heard the slap of Slarda's bow again. The cat seemed to give no muscular movement, it sprang stiff-legged, it levitated, and the bolt whined under it, a yellow wasp, and struck the sand with a kapok sound. The cat had twisted in its jump. Now it faced Slarda. It began to step carelessly towards her. It was *strolling*. Susan leaned forward, she whispered, 'Cat.' For now she saw the marks on its side, the four raked scars running from shoulder to hip, pink and sore and tender in the hair. And saw the mark worn by a collar on its neck. This was him, this was the one. It was the cat the High Priest had kept, and ordered to kill her. The cat Ben had fought, and clawed on its side. And she had taken its collar off and sent it home. And here it was, in its jungle, on its sands — hunting Slarda. She watched. She knew the woman had no chance. She felt sorry for her and wanted to save her, but telling her to run would serve no purpose.

'Cat,' she whispered, 'please don't kill her.'

'Cat,' she called.

It made no sign, but kept its lazy walk towards the woman. Slarda had reloaded. Thirty metres of sand separated her from the animal. She began a rearward creeping. If she was afraid she did not show it. Her eyes never blinked. She was a savage creature too. Her lips were drawn back from her teeth. The closer she let the cat come the better her chance. Her shot had to strike and had to kill.

The cat advanced. Ten body-lengths away it stopped. Its tail grew rigid, its back arched. Its ears were flattened on its head. Stiff-legged, almost clumsy, it turned side-on, inviting Slarda to shoot. She shook her head and took a half step back. No, she would not shoot, not yet. 'Closer, red one. I'll have your skin.' Her whisper came to Susan across the sand. The cat seemed to dance then, came in closer, stiff-legged still, head angled low. Again it offered its side to Slarda. And now the woman acted: in one movement aimed and shot. It was her chance, the best she would have. The speed of the bolt must beat the cat.

Somehow Susan was there, she was in the Bloodcat's mind, and knew it beat the woman not the bolt. Its spring began at pressure, not release — so it was gone before the bolt was launched, Slarda shot at nothing. Yet she was clever, and allowed for the movement; shot high, and the bolt came close. Its feathers brushed the Bloodcat's belly at the peak of its jump. Then the cat was down, and running: four, five steps, then a bound. It came at Slarda high, dropping at her, and Slarda, in a crouch, knife in hand, reached up to slash the animal's belly. She hoped to disembowel it. But in that upward look her throat was bared. It was enough. The cat flicked with a back leg, with claw unsheathed like a gutting knife, and cut her throat. Slarda fell, and rolled over once, and beat her shins on the sand. She lay dead. It was very simple, very quick. The cat turned from its landing place. It walked to her, and sniffed, and sat down and licked its back paw clean.

'Slarda,' Susan whispered, 'I'm sorry, Slarda.' She closed her eyes. She was so tired, so worn out in her feelings, that she was not able to move or think. She did not even open

78

her eyes again. She felt the cat coming close. She felt it sitting in front of her, looking, waiting. She had no idea what it would do, and did not care. Then it seemed to her she slept a while. When she opened her eyes the cat was there, resting too. Slarda's body sprawled indistinct on the sand. A narrow shadow pressed at the foot of the dune. Susan's face and torso lay in it, but her legs were burning in the sun. She looked at the cat. She did not think it would be wise to move. 'Cat,' she whispered. It opened its eyes and looked at her. They seemed cooler, and the pupils, though shrinking in the light, were blunt at the tips.

'Cat,' she said, 'I'm getting up.'

It watched her while she stood, then it stood too.

'Cat, if you're going to kill me, do it now.'

The animal twitched its tail, but gave no sign.

She said, 'Do you remember the arena? And Ben? And me taking off your collar?'

The cat looked bored. It yawned again. It seemed fond of yawning, this cat. She knew she was not getting through to it. 'Cat, how do I talk to you? Why aren't I scared? Are you my friend?' She took a step towards it. That made it act. It stiffened, showed a flash of tooth under its lip. 'No, not yet. Not friends.'

She tried to think what to do. Jimmy had talked to Ben in pictures — and she too had learned to show, not tell. So . . . Carefully, keeping it simple, she made a picture of the arena: banks of spectators, tongue of stone over the drop, the dais, the High Priest. And the cat gave a screech. It leaned at her, trembling. It had memories, that was plain. She made more pictures, in a hurry: herself unbuckling the collar, freeing the cat. And the cat running, leaping up the steps of the arena, while the priests parted frantically to let it through. And the leap from arena to cliff-top, and the jungle beckoning. That was it. She flashed it like a series of slides for the cat to see. And it saw. Somehow it saw. It relaxed. The tension went out of it. It settled more easily on its legs.

'Cat,' Susan said, 'I set you free.'

As if in answer, the cat closed its eyes, and opened them. It was, she saw, a sign of trust. But she could not help wondering what would happen when the animal grew hungry. Would the slide-show work?

Her head was aching and her mouth was dry. It was not easy making these pictures. They must take a lot from her, for when she moved she seemed to have no strength. 'Water,' she said. 'Cat, I need water.' She looked at Slarda's body, and though she did not want to see it close walked towards it. The cat gave a growl, but she made another picture: a pool of water. That quietened it. She came to Slarda's body and was glad it was lying face down. She did not want to see the woman's throat. She unfastened her water flask from her belt and drank from it. The water was warm, but ran down her throat sweet as honey. She drank deeply, then poured a little water in her hand and offered it to the cat. The animal turned its back. It strolled away and lay on the sand.

Careful, Susan told herself, not too fast.

She unstrapped Slarda's food pouch and retrieved her knife from where it had fallen. The woman's leather cap had fallen off and her hair was spread on the sand. Brown hair, pretty hair. What had turned Slarda into a killer? What was it in her, and the others, that allowed them to kill so easily, and enjoy it? She belted on the knife and pouch and flask. That was all she wanted. She did not want to take the woman's blanket or her cap, though both would be useful. Then she remembered Steen. She looked into the desert and shivered. She did not want to go, but knew she must. Slarda might have wounded him, not killed him. He might be lying there, dying slowly. She had to make sure.

'Cat,' she said, 'I'm going to find my friend. Are you coming?' It seemed best to pretend he was safe. He padded along behind her, and although he might be waiting his time to kill she would behave as though he was friendly. She followed Slarda's steps back into the dunes. They kept a straight line, and her own trail lay alongside, denting the sand. Then she came to a place where they had parted — or rather, where Slarda's had joined hers again. The woman had angled across from a crowd of little conical hills. A good place for an ambush, though they'd done Steen no good. She went into them and found the sand packed harder, mixed with earth and pebbles. She lost the trail. 'Where?' she said to the Bloodcat. It stood behind whipping its tail. 'Help me,' she said. 'You can find him.' She made a picture of Steen lying on the sand, with his arms outflung. It galvanized the cat, made it leap into the air as though stung. It growled and advanced on her. She saw the way its joints worked under its hide, so beautifully. It made her feel clumsy; but she formed the picture again, and tried to show herself and the animal there too.

The cat understood. It seemed to nod, and it raised its nose, sniffing the air, and started off round the nearest hill. It led her a long way, further than she thought Steen could have gone. But there he was — and just has she had shown him in her picture, arms out-stretched. It was as if she had known. She walked towards him beside the cat. He was in a little hollow, like something dead lying in a basin. She felt tears of pity for him, and of anger at the waste. Steen dead. Slarda too. There was no need, they should be alive. She knelt beside him and said, 'Steen, I'm sorry.' And suddenly she seemed to be speaking with a voice not her own — an O voice not an Earth voice, and words she had

81

not thought. 'I'll try to stop it all, I promise you. No more killing.' His mouth was wide in his shout of pain. His eyes stared blindly at the sun. She tried to close them but could not make the lids go all the way.

The cat sniffed at him and turned away. It sat on the sand and yawned. It did not want Steen for food – but ants would pick him clean. Scouts had already found him. She saw them busy underneath, by the broken shaft of Slarda's bolt. Steen would be a skeleton, dry bones in the desert. She did not see anything wrong with that, it might be an end he would have chosen. But she wanted some way of saying goodbye. So she picked up a handful of sand and let it trickle on his chest – a kind of burial. No prayers; O had had more than enough of that. She said, 'Goodbye, Steen. Thank you for helping me. I'm glad you were your own man, not Osro's.' It seemed enough. She turned away and walked towards the jungle. The cat padded easily, two or three steps ahead.

They took a new way and did not see Slarda again. It was further to the jungle than Susan had thought and she wondered if the cat knew where it was going. Perhaps it preferred to stay in the desert. In that case she would have to get away. She must reach the coast and find the Birdfolk. 'Cat,' she said, 'jungle.' She made a picture of creepers and trees. The cat growled. Did that mean yes? It did not change its course but kept straight on; and soon she saw the dark line of trees. 'Good,' she said, stepping faster, coming up to the animal's side. Without thinking, she let her hand fall on its neck.

The cat's reaction was so swift she never knew what had happened. She felt a blow on her side that knocked the breath out of her and sent her spinning across the sand in a tangle of arms and legs. She did not know how long she lay, spitting sand, wiping it from her eyes. But when she was able to see she rose on her hands and knees and faced the cat. It crouched two metres away, eyes burning, ears flat, teeth bared in the sun. One wrong move or word and it would spring. She must say and do exactly what was right, or she would die. But even as she prepared herself, she took hope from the thought that the cat had struck with its claws still sheathed, otherwise she would be dead already.

'Cat,' she whispered, 'I'm your friend,' and she made the picture at the same time: the girl, herself, unbuckling the collar, freeing the cat. Again, again she made it, keeping it simple. This was a primitive animal, much more primitive and savage than Ben. It must have only a few simple thoughts, a few responses. Attack! Kill! Tear! Eat! How could friendship be one of them? She must keep reinforcing its memory of her setting it free. That was the only pathway she had into its mind.

In a little while she stood up. 'Now,' she whispered, 'we're friends. You don't want me touching you. But friends touch.' She made the picture: her hand coming down to rest on its head. The cat snarled. It sank a little deeper in its crouch. 'Stay,' she said 'you stay there.' She moved several steps towards it. She held out her hand to show what she meant to do; advanced it until it was a hand-width from the cat. She let it stay there. It trembled and she told it to stop. When she moved it again the cat struck. Yet it shortened its blow, something held it back. The tip of one claw nicked Susan's wrist, blood dripped on the sand. It was a dangerous moment. Blood might madden the cat.

Slowly Susan withdrew her hand and pushed out the other. The cat struck again, knocked it aside, but this time the claws were sheathed. 'No' she said. She brought her hand back. The cat pushed it away. 'See, we're touching.' She made a picture: paw and hand. The cat seemed to think about it. It seemed to grow sulky, and moved back a step.

Carefully, Susan closed the gap, brought herself back in touching range. 'Now,' she said, 'I'll touch your head. If you and I are friends we've got to touch.' She showed him herself with her hand on his head. He drew back his lip at that, but made no move. She advanced her hand; she let her fingertips come down just above his eyes. His ears flattened, that was all, he made a spitting sound, like tearing paper. But he allowed it.

After a while she moved her hand and cupped it on his head. Taking care not to move suddenly, she stepped round to his side and touched the mark left by the collar on his neck. She knelt and looked at the scars on his side. The cuts were tender still but they were healing. 'Ben really got you.' She made a picture of the Varg, and the cat made no response. He did not seem to bear Ben any malice.

'Now,' Susan said, 'we're friends. We can travel together. But you've got to have a name. I can't call you Cat.' She thought a while, and remembered the barn cats at home, Poorman and Beggarman. Once there had been Richman — Richman lived in the house — but he was dead. She smiled at the cat. 'How about Thief? It seems to suit you.'

The cat moved off and cleaned its paw. She licked her own wrist where the claw had nicked it. 'You're dangerous,' she said. 'I'm glad you're on my side.' She hoped he was. She did not think they were really friends yet, or if they were it was not a friendship she was going to count on. Something could easily tip it over — hunger could. She looked at Thief licking his claw — getting a taste of her blood — and wondered when he would be hungry next.

'Come on, Thief. Let's get moving.' She made another picture of the jungle; and surprisingly, making her start, something came back — a picture from Thief, the first he had sent. It had no colour but was black and white, and that, she supposed, showed how primitive Bloodcats were.

Ben's pictures were in colour. But this showed jungle like an old photograph. The point of it, she saw, was that the wall of sand was low. Thief was showing an easy way in.

'Good,' she whispered, 'let's go.'

They moved towards the jungle and turned along its edge, and the wall of sand shrank until it was level with her head. Thief turned and leaped to the top of it. She recognized the place he had shown her. She scrambled up and joined him and he started into the trees. 'Stop, stop,' she said. They were going too fast. She had to think. She knew where she was heading but not why. The things she would do when she found the Birdfolk were no longer clear. Once it had been a matter of getting back to the cave and going home. But now she had made Steen a promise. Between her and home was job she must do – stop the killing. How could she have said that? There was nothing she could do to stop an army – and this army had the fire Weapon, and troops that looked as savage as Tartar horsemen, the Mongol horde. Yet when she had spoken it was as if she spoke from some knowledge.

In spite of Thief's presence she felt alone. The desert gleamed like a lake of salt. Ahead the forest – mossy aisles, black trunks – made a humming silence that seemed to empty all thought from her head. She could not believe humans had ever passed this way. And she needed humans, she needed friends, she had to talk, and find out what it was she had to do. She knew her bond with O was a special one. Twice she had been called, and somehow not completed her task. Now it seemed three was the special number. Three would make things whole. But what must she do?

It seemed to her Jimmy would not know; or Nick. Or Limpy or his father. They were too practical, too violent. The Birdfolk might. They belonged on O. And Ben, the

Varg. And Soona — especially her. She seemed to have intuitive knowledge. And the Woodlanders. They had it too. A knowledge and a wisdom thousands of years old, bred in them by their long communion with O. She must find Woodlanders, and find Soona.

'Thief,' she said. The animal was waiting patiently. She projected an image of Dawn, the Woodlander girl. 'Find one, Thief. Find a Woodlander for me. But you mustn't kill. Do they live in this jungle?'

The Bloodcat watched, still-eyed, and gave no sign of understanding. She supposed that meant the answer was no; and she could not remember the Woodlanders talking of villages this far north. So it seemed she would have to find Birdfolk, and travel to Wildwood or the Temple. She hoped there would be enough time. Osro's army was mobilizing. Soon he would be making his Weapon. Then it was too late.

'Thief,' she said, 'take me to the coast. The quickest way.' She pictured a beach, with small waves, yellow sand, driftwood line, and bush and cliffs at the back of it — any beach. Thief seemed to understand, and she found his own picture in her mind: a bar, a river mouth, in that uncoloured state that still did not make them seem dead. 'Yes,' she said, 'that's it,' and took the image, placed herself in it, with Thief at her side, walking on the bar.

Thief turned. It appeared he meant to stay with her and guide her — be her friend? She wasn't sure. Watching him amble ahead, turning a deeper red in the shade of the trees, she could not believe anything so savage could ever be friend. But he was companion, at least for the moment. She decided not to think any further than that.

She drank more water as she walked behind him, and ate a strip of meat from Slarda's pouch. When they came to a stream she knelt to fill the flask, but Thief gave a growl.

She took it as a warning and looked more closely in the water. Tiny transparent things, smaller than mosquito larvae, swarmed almost invisible. She wondered what they would have done to her stomach, and she dipped her finger in. The sting was more fierce than a wasp sting and she shrieked; and was aware, even in her pain, that Thief gave a sympathetic howl. She sucked her finger, trying to draw the poison out. 'Thief,' she said – or moaned – 'you saved my life.'

The Bloodcat came and nudged her, pushed her along. There was something urgent in his behaviour. He loped between the trees and she ran to keep up. Her finger was swelling and a pain began in the bones of her wrist. Thief leaped up a bank. He stood on the top, nosing something. 'What is it?' Susan said. 'Do you want me up there?' She was feeling dizzy and the pain in her hand was worse. All the fingers were swelling. Thief jumped down. He butted her, forced her at the bank. She began to climb. It was difficult, she could only use one arm, and the pain in the other made her whimper. It had got to her elbow. Someone was squeezing it with tongs.

She reached the top of the bank and fell on her knees. She knew in a moment she would faint, her head was swinging round and round. But she saw Thief, swelling like a balloon, and by his nose a small red mushroom or toadstool. It pulsed like a tiny heart. Thief's tongue flicked out and touched it. 'I can't eat that, it's poisonous,' Susan whispered. But again his tongue went flick, pink and sharp. It knocked the mushroom's head off its stalk and pushed it at her. She fumbled for it, felt it break in her fingers. Its smell was vinegary, and in her mouth the taste was foul. But her stomach craved and she swallowed greedily and felt at once a battle start in her. Two things were fighting for her life. Her head spun faster, she seemed to be rolling over and over, and shooting off into space. Then everything was still, suddenly. It was as though her heart, her breathing, stopped; and she gave a huge gulp and started them. The pain in her arm throbbed easily. She knew the battle was over, she was not going to die; and she crawled a little way to a bed of grass and lay curled up. She saw Thief sitting on the other side, his urgency gone. He was indifferent again.

'It's dangerous, this jungle,' she whispered. 'But I'm all right. I've got you to look after me.'

Thief yawned. He lay down and closed his eyes. She closed hers too, and at once she slept.

It took three days to reach the coast. Susan made do with fruit and the few strips of meat in Slarda's pouch. Thief found safe water for her to drink. The Bloodcat hunted in the dawn. Once she lay in her fern bed and heard the hideous sound of him killing nearby. He came back heavy with meat, satisfied, and for a while she could not look at him. But later in the day they entered a drier forest, where everything was red or brown, and tough and dry. She almost lost him as he went ahead, he was invisible in the dappled shade. Here, she supposed, was his native place, and nothing that he did seemed cruel or wrong.

Her right hand was puffy, but swimming in the salt lagoon at the back of the beach made it feel better. They went down to the bar — it was just as Thief had shown her — and watched the long rollers crashing in. This was more like home than any place Susan had been and she felt a surge of longing for Earth. But she controlled it, and searched the sky, looking for Birdfolk. It was empty. A bird like a shag sat on a rock, gulls stood further out on the bar, that was all.

All that day she watched. She began to lose hope. Where

had they gone? They knew she was alive, why weren't they looking? Then she remembered the Seafolk and tried calling them. But none seemed to live on this part of the coast. There was none of the yellow weed that was their food and so no reason for them to come.

'What am I going to do, Thief?'

She climbed around the rocks at the south end of the beach. Far away, islands smudged the horizon. She wondered how many days' travel she was from the Temple. It seemed she would have to make it there alone – alone with Thief.

They came to another beach. It was just a few metres of sand enclosed in cliffs. 'We'll have to go inland. Will you come with me, Thief?' She did not dare show him the Temple. Then, across the sand, she saw a cave. It was set halfway up the cliff, partly hidden by trees that blazed with red flowers.

'I wonder,' she said. 'Do you think any Stonefolk live in there?' She could not show pictures of Stonefolk – she had never seen them, no one had – but showed Thief an image of the cave, the blackness of a deep interior, and heard him growl. She saw the hairs prickle on his spine. She guessed that somehow he had picked up her thought of Stonefolk. He did not like it.

'They're our friends, Thief.' She knew she must try to talk with them. Just as much as Woodlanders, they had that old wisdom of O. They might know what she had to do. 'Thief, come with me.' She jumped down to the beach and crossed the sand and climbed up through the trees to the cave. It might be just a shallow one, but if it was she would look for another. She wondered why she hadn't thought of Stonefolk sooner.

The mouth was wide enough to let her go in side by side with Thief. He set up a rumbling growl but stepped in without hesitating. It was a long cave and soon they were in semi-darkness. Thief stopped. 'What is it, Thief? Is something there?' She was not scared of any animal while she had the Bloodcat. But it was a rockfall that had stopped him. She saw it as her eyes got used to the dark. It blocked the cave and left no way through. She climbed it and up by the ceiling found a place where air seemed to shift. She could see no opening but put her mouth where she thought it might be.

'Stonefolk, are you there?' she called. There was no reply, and she did not expect one straight away. They took their time, they would not be hurried. But if any lived in this part of O they would answer. 'Stonefolk, I'm your friend. We've met before. I'm Susan Ferris. I know I've got to help O again and I want to know how. Can you tell me?'

This time an answer came. It startled her and made Thief howl. The voice was close, in the dark on the other side of the fall. It was younger, less furry, than other Stonefolk voices she had heard. 'Susan Ferris?'

'Yes.'

'You have a beast with you?'

'Yes, a Bloodcat. His name's Thief. He's my friend.'

'No one can make friends with a Bloodcat.'

'Well, he's here, right by my side. And he's not eating me. But you sound as if you were waiting. Who are you? What's your name?'

'I have none yet, I have not earned one. I am simply daughter of Deep Delver. But Susan, listen to me. All through Stone the Folk are waiting, at every exit into Light. We wait for you, for one who has held in her hands the wisdom and strength of Freeman Wells.'

'Why? Why do you wait?'

'We know of your capture and escape. There is very little

Stonefolk do not know. But where you escaped to was a mystery. Now you are here. And looking for us.'

'Yes,' Susan said. She swallowed. It was as if she had already seen what was to happen but could not bring it into her mind. Something she was fated to do — something that would turn O upside-down. 'Humans are killing each other again. I made a promise to stop it. But I don't know how.'

There was a silence. Then the Stonewoman sighed. 'It is worse than you know. It is worse than killing. And yes, you have a task. It is prophesied. I know what it is — but how you perform it, that will be told by others, not by me. Listen now. We have heard —' she seemed to shudder '— that a human, one who was priest, has found a new way to make the Weapon. We thought that knowledge buried so deep it would never be found. Freeman Wells saw how it could be done — and if it was, he saw that O would die. So he banished it, cast it out, and gave the words of it, and all the bits of metal, paper, stone, the acid and the oil, all to us, the Stonefolk, and commanded us to bury it so deep it would be lost until the end of time. Susan — ' the Stonewoman seemed to be crying now, 'Susan, we took it all, our Wisewomen and Wisemen, we took it and carried it far, to the very deepest place on O. There lies a pit that dives even deeper. None have ever found the bottom of it. We have dropped down pebbles, boulders, and never heard them strike. It drops forever. And there they cast the knowledge — into nothing. And came away believing it would never be known again.'

Susan did not know what to say. The Stonewoman's grief seemed excessive. But Thief understood it. He set up a trembling moan in time with her voice.

'And now,' the Stonewoman said, 'it has come again. One has thought out all the words again, and all the symbols, and gathered up the parts – and he is not a man like Freeman Wells. He will use it. O will die.'

'Why?' Susan whispered. 'Why will it?'

'This Weapon will burn the hills and mountains. Burn living Stone. And . . .'

'Yes, go on.'

'The smoke will rise up and darken the sky – I do not understand it, this sky, but Freeman Wells, he said that the fiery orb that floats in it, that gives all life to those who dwell in Light, will hide itself and not be seen again, and all the darkened skies and all the seas will turn to poison. Stone too. Stone will sicken. Stone will die.' The woman wept unashamedly. 'And if there are two, and these Weapons meet, then a burning starts that will have no end. Everything will burn – and burn – and burn – and only dead ashes will be left. That will be O.'

Susan crouched on the rock pile. She found her arm locked around Thief's neck. The moaning of the Bloodcat filled her ears. She whispered, 'Why did you wait? Why do you want me?'

The Stonewoman sniffed and swallowed. Susan heard a bristly sound as she rubbed her face. 'Freeman Wells said if this Weapon came, if men ever thought of it and put it together, then O was lost, unless –' she sighed – 'there was one who could stop it.'

'Go on.'

'One who knew the way to hold all Humankind in her hands.'

'Her?'

'He said her.'

'And you think it's me?'

'It seemed to us – to our Wisewomen and Wisemen – that Susan Ferris was the one. Because she had the Mark on her wrist, because she held the Halves, because she stood by the Motherstone, wrapped in light. And if we are wrong — there is no other.'

Thief leaned on Susan. He seemed to agree. She tried to understand what the Stonewoman said — there was a thing in it she already knew — but fear stopped her thinking.

'How?' she stammered. 'Where do I go? And how much time?'

'Little time. The word comes now. Let me listen. Through veins of Stone the whisper comes. Ah no! No! It is made. The Weapon is made. He tries it on forests and the hills. He burns it deep, and makes the rivers boil. Little time. He will go south, and attack the army of the Freemen. And now! And now!' She gave a cry. 'The word comes now. The Freemen learn the secret. They will make the Weapon. O is lost.'

Thief gave a great wild howl.

'Stop it, stop it, both of you,' Susan cried. 'I've got to think, I've got to know.'

Thief fell silent, and slowly the sobbing of the Stonewoman stopped.

'You said others would tell me what to do. Where are they? Where do I go?'

'South,' the Stonewoman said. 'One day south. You will find a lake, where it meets the sea. Off the coast are islands — Thousand Isles, and among them one called Furthermost. Freeman Wells had his home there. And there is the tale of what you must do.'

'How will I find it?'

'At the place where fresh meets salt call for the People of the Sea. They will come, they will take you.'

'Is that all?'

'Yes. Go now. Go.'

'I will. Stonewoman?'

'I have a name now. I am Weeper.'

'If anyone comes asking in a cave, asking for me, and if it's Jimmy Jaspers or Nick Quinn – tell them where I am.'

'I will send the word.'

'And when they come – tell them not to leave Soona behind.'

'Soona?'

'Yes, Soona. She must come.' She did not know why, but she felt it was the most important thing she had ever said.

She turned and went out towards the light, with Thief beside her.

CHAPTER SEVEN

Furthermost

Silverwing and Yellowclaw came swooping out of the dawn light. Morning mist had dampened their wings. They landed on the shingle bank by the river and walked across to Jimmy's fire.

'The lake is half a day's walk, and the sea lies beyond. Islands spread out in a great circle. One of your boats would take a day and night to sail across. How will you reach this Furthermost?'

Jimmy raked his meat from the fire. 'You tell me.' He glanced at Soona, sitting on the other side with Dawn. 'That Stone geezer didn' give no hint. Go to Furthermost in the Thousand Isles. That was it. You'da thought he had lockjaw.'

Soona looked up from the embers. 'He said that I must go, Susan needed me. He said no other word had come to him. But that she had asked for Nick and Jimmy.'

'Well, here we are,' Jimmy growled, 'and it looks like we're gunner have ter swim. Any houses on these islands?'

'No,' Yellowclaw said. 'A few fishermen's huts, but no one lives in them. We saw the outer islands where this Furthermost must lie. Nothing is there.'

Nick swallowed the piece of meat he was chewing. 'If the Stonefolk say Susan's there, she's there.' He had no doubt of it. Since meeting the Stoneman Seeker, who had saved him and Susan from the Priests of Ferris (and died from the luminous dial of Nick's watch), he had looked on Stonefolk as having special knowledge. If Susan was in their care she was all right. He was more concerned about Soona. The girl seemed to be waiting for something, preparing.

Nick could tell she was afraid, and Dawn too found something strange in her. It was as if, she said, some new thing was growing in Soona, like a flower, but though its bloom was beautiful its roots fed on her life. That meant nothing to Nick, it was too poetic. He wanted to know what she was thinking about all the time, but when he asked she told him she was making up tunes – and remembering old ones. To prove it she played them on her flute. The Varg swayed and nodded in time with the rhythms. They moved about Soona with gentleness and slowness. It was as if they looked on her as a special person, but when he tried to question them they sent no pictures back. Dawn confessed that her friend – Nick had named her Bess and no one minded – would not speak of Soona with her. It was all very strange and it worried Nick and made him angry.

Silverwing said, 'There's another thing. Osro's army has sent bands of scouts out. One of them is camped on the north side of the lake. Fifteen warriors, men and women. They are Hotlanders, not at home in these forests, and they make no attempt to hide themselves. But when they come round the lake they will find your trail.'

'We better be gone then,' Jimmy said. 'I'd sooner tangle with Bloodcats than them geezers.'

They dowsed their fire and shouldered their packs. The Varg came out of the trees, where they had been hunting, and the band set off down-river. Yellowclaw and Silverwing flew low overhead, keeping a ridge between them and the Hotlander camp. By noon they reached the lake. It was several kilometres wide and vanished round a bend towards the sea. On the southern side the land went sweeping up to the summit of a flat-topped hill which the Birdfolk said ran along to cliffs on the shore. Several ways led down to the sea, and on the rocks the yellow weed grew. Seafolk lived there.

They climbed to the top of the hill and started along. It was as flat as a table, but prickly scrub growing head-high prevented them from seeing lake or sea. Yellowclaw and Silverwing kept to the south, out of sight. Ben broke a trail, crushing bushes flat with his paws.

They came to the plateau rim in mid-afternoon, broke through the scrub, and saw the sea. The sight made them gasp. It was as if someone had flung islands out in a handful. Some were small, no more than smooth-topped rocks standing a metre or two clear of the water. Others, equally low, managed to grow trees or grass and from the cliff-top looked like enamelled shields, or basking monsters growing forest patches on their backs. Five or six large islands lay amongst them, stretching arms. They reached out to the horizon. Channels made a web between, deep blue, almost purple. It would take years, Nick thought, to land on each. But only one of them was Furthermost.

'There's more than a bloddy thousand,' Jimmy said. 'There's millions.'

'The Seafolk will know which one,' Dawn said.

Nick looked south down the coast. Far away, beyond the haze, was a grey smudge of land. He wondered if it was the cape where the Seafolk had saved Susan from the whirlpool. If so, the swamp lay inland, and Sheercliff and the Temple further in; and the city where Otis Claw had ruled was south again. The cave in the mountain, where he and Susan must travel when he found her, seemed so far away he could not imagine reaching it – and Earth, for a moment, was beyond memory.

'She's a big land,' Jimmy said. 'She'll do me.'

'Not me,' Nick said. 'I'm from Earth. I'm going back.'

'Give 'em my love,' Jimmy said. 'Here come the Pollies. I hope they've found an easy way down.'

Silverwing and Yellowclaw came beating up from the

shoreline. They rode on a current out from the rim and Yellowclaw cried, 'The Seafolk are waiting. They have a boat. But you must hurry. The Hotlanders saw me as I flew down. See, by the lake, they are coming.'

Nick shaded his eyes. The lake ended in a short river that flowed to the sea. It cut through a yellow beach, and there he saw what seemed to be a coloured centipede. It ran, it ran fast, with legs flickering in the sun. It took him a moment to make out the parts – men and women, red and blue. Their heads and breasts gleamed like an insect's shell, their long spears bristled like antennae. They came to the river and ran through. Broken water flashed in the sun.

'Yeah,' Jimmy said, 'they got our scent. An' they're butchers, every one. Let's make ourselves scarce.'

Silverwing guided them, while Yellowclaw flew down to keep watch on the Hotlanders. She took them along the rim and down the sweep of land to cliffs rising sheer from the sea. There she led them to a giant landslip, where the bears found a path through boulders to a stony beach held in the curve of two reefs. Beyond the narrow opening islands lay. A boat was nosed on the shingle and the heads of Seafolk showed on the waterline like a string of buoys.

'Get aboard, they're coming,' Silverwing cried. Nick looked up to the top of the slip and saw the Hotlanders. Their speed seemed impossible. Their long thin legs, their fleshless arms, jointed in a way that seemed unhuman, terrified him. Yellowclaw was overhead, loosing arrows. Silverwing flew to help. They kept out of spear range and sent down a stream of arrows, trying to slow the Hotlanders, but it barely made them pause. They carried small oval shields buckled on their forearms and with these warded off the arrows. Their speed of limb and eye seemed unnatural. Savage, primitive; yet to Nick they seemed like

98

something from the future – humans mass-produced by a machine. Their shaven skulls gleamed like plastic bowls.

'In,' Jimmy yelled. He picked Nick up and hurled him into the boat. Soona and Dawn were already in, and Jimmy vaulted up like a boy and turned to face the land with his axe. The boat was wide and flat, with a low deck-house. It was more barge than yacht and its heaviness held it on the stones. The Seafolk strained along the sides but it moved only an inch or two. Then the Varg, Bess and Ben, added their strength. They put their paws on the bow and heaved and the barge grated out and floated free. They plunged into the water, keeping it going, and together, Seafolk and Varg, they drove the heavy craft at the gap in the reef.

The Hotlanders were almost at the beach. One huge man – he must, Nick thought, be two metres tall – jumped on a boulder and hurled his spear. It came on a flat trajectory and hissed into the sea a boat length short. His shout of anger came as shrill as a gull's cry. No one else threw. They ran. They burst on to the beach and made no pause, but were in the black rocks of the reef. One fell with an arrow in his leg. They were not pausing to ward off arrows now.

'Inside,' Jimmy yelled. 'They're gunner be in range.' He pushed Soona and Dawn into the deck-house. Nick followed and Jimmy came in last. 'Keep down from that winder. Yer'll get skewered.' He pushed Nick down. They heard the hissing again, and the thud of spears striking the barge at the waterline. The Hotlanders were attacking the Seafolk. The barge lurched and halted, then moved more heavily.

'The Seafolk have gone round the other side. Ben and Bess too,' Dawn said. She and Jimmy were getting messages. Nick felt pressure on the keel. It must be hard keeping the barge straight, but he knew the Varg would get them through. The Hotlanders would come up though almost to point-blank range. He crouched as low as he could, close to the wall. Dawn and Soona lay beside him and Jimmy was on the other side of the window, near the door. Now and then he risked a glance out the window.

'Gettin' close. But we're gunner make it.' A spear hissed by his face and struck the wall. 'O.K. Keep down. It's us they're pottin'.' Spears struck the deck-house. Several pierced the wood and jutted like nails into the room. Others, in a flight – five, seven – came through the window and stood trembling in the wall and floor. Long spears, iron tipped, with shafts that seemed to hum, and spiky feathers tied below the head.

'Use up yer ammo,' Jimmy said. But each warrior had four or five spears. The attack went on, the spears in the room stood as thick as hair and the window was framed in shining points. At last it stopped. A cry came from above the boat. 'No more spears,' – Yellowclaw. Jimmy and Nick looked out the window. The reef was only ten metres away, with Hotlanders crowded by the water. The barge had passed the closest point. They had missed their chance to jump for it.

'What are they doing?'

'Dunno,' Jimmy said. He went outside and the others followed. The Hotlanders broke into two groups. A man uncoiled a rope and ran it between them. It was as if they meant to have a tug of war. But they lowered the rope until it touched the ground. Now they seemed about to spin it for skipping. But Jimmy yelled, 'They're gunner chuck 'im at us.' A Hotlander crouched further back – one smaller than the others, just a boy. He began to run. Yellowclaw and Silverwing had seen the danger too. They let fly arrows at him, but his start was too swift. The arrows struck the reef and bounced away. The boy was at the rope, his foot was on it, and he leaped. At the same time the warriors heaved and the rope jerked tight with such force it snapped in two. The timing for a feat like that was so fine Nick could not believe it – yet the boy was thrown twenty metres. He made a red flash in the air, and with arms stretched out came down at the barge like a dragon-fly. His fingers found the rail and locked on it, his legs splashed in the sea. For a moment he trailed, then hauled himself up. He was coiled like a spring at the rail, and he reached for the knife clamped in his teeth.

The Varg had swum to the rear of the boat and they lunged at him. From overhead, Yellowclaw and Silverwing shot arrows. Just for a moment their target was still. One took the boy in the shoulder, the other struck him above the hip. The shock made him cry out and his knife fell into the sea. For a second or two he clung to the rail with one hand. Then he let go and splashed into the water, staining it red. The Varg plunged forward, but Seafolk lifted the Hotlander clear and made a raft of bodies under him. One, lifting her head, croaked in her painful voice, 'We do not kill. It is not our way. We will return him to his people.'

'If yer do he's a goner,' Jimmy said. 'They sent 'im ter take out some of us and he ballsed it up. They'll chop 'im in little pieces.'

'Bring him here,' Soona said. 'We won't hurt him.'

'He is dying,' Dawn said. 'I must treat his wounds.'

The Seafolk brought the boy to the side of the boat and lifted him, standing like dolphins on their tails. Nick and Jimmy grabbed him and pulled him on board. The boy was conscious. He twisted and flapped like a fish and would have got free, but Ben climbed on to the barge and held him down with a paw on his chest. Dawn knelt beside him. She looked at his wounds, which leaked blood on the deck, and said, 'Nick, my pack. I must make him sleep. Then I must close these wounds or he will have no blood left.' The boy's eyes, glazing over, still had life to look at her. No trace of fear showed. His lips snarled and he made a feeble bite at her hand. 'Nick.' He ran into the deck-house. Soona came and looked over Dawn's shoulder.

'He's so young.'

Her voice convulsed the boy. It was as if she had splashed scalding liquid on him. His eyes jerked to her face, widened as though from a blinding pain, and his mouth screamed. An eruption of strength ran through his body, jerking him from under Ben's paw. His wounds were nothing. He was on his feet as quick as a cat, before the bear could move, and he tore the arrow from the wound on his hip, and holding it like a dagger sprang at Soona. Dawn was quickest. She caught the boy's arm and hung on it, and was dragged along. She slowed his thrust so that Soona was able to twist and the arrow pierced her robe. Then Jimmy was there, with a bellow, and Nick, coming from the deck-house, and Ben too, and they wrestled and beat the boy down. Finally they had him on the deck. It was like trying to hold a greased wrestler, Nick thought. He lay on the arm that held the arrow, putting all his weight on, but it twisted like an eel, and it took all his strength to hold it down. 'Kill,' screamed the boy, his eyes on Soona, 'enemy, kill.' Ben held him with claws unsheathed and Jimmy lay on his legs. 'Soona, my bag,' Dawn cried. 'The bottle. Quick.' Soona thrust it into her hand and Dawn poured liquid in her palm and cupped it on the boy's nose. He gasped. He sighed. He slept. But still his teeth were bared and spasms of rage and ferocity twitched the muscles in his cheeks.

'You can let him go.'

Cautiously they freed him and stood up. The boy lay sleeping, twitching, while Dawn worked on his shoulder and hip. She poured a sweet-smelling oil in the wounds, then smeared on a pungent cream. The blood stopped oozing. Next she sprinkled black and white powder on them. It's a recipe, Nick thought sourly. There's the pepper and salt. He wasn't very fond of this Hotlander. He'd done his best to kill them and now they were busy saving his life. His thinness and hairlessness seemed unhuman, and his colour, his red skin, was like a disease. It was the red of strawberries, and though Nick knew it was paint, he shivered. On the boy's chest a bright blue lightning bolt was tattooed.

'Means he's a man,' Jimmy said. 'They got some ceremony where they hold 'em down and cut it in with bits of glass. Hurts like hell. Poor little sod.'

'He's not so little. If this is Osro's army the Freemen have got no chance.'

'It ain't gunner be that sort of war.'

'No,' Nick said. He looked at the blue lightning on the boy's chest. The Weapon, Osro's Weapon, Kenno's Weapon, meant that warriors — swords, spears, arrows — were out-of-date. He left Dawn working and Jimmy keeping guard and turned to the land. On the reef the Hotlanders stood in a circle. Even at a distance of several hundred metres they were threatening. They swayed in unison, a ritual of some kind, some working out of rage or frustration. They seemed like a giant sea anemone, waiting for prey. Further off, at the cliff, Yellowclaw was retrieving arrows while Silverwing kept watch. Ben, trusting Dawn's sleeping potion, had slipped back into the sea and was chasing fish with Bess. The Varg were always hungry. Along the sides of the barge the Seafolk laboured. Others swam further off, waiting their turn. Already the nearest island was sliding by. Nick hoped that when Dawn had finished her doctoring they could stop and put the boy on an island, let him fend for himself. He was dangerous. Nick knew he would never forget the savagery — the Bloodcat savagery — with which he had gone for Soona.

He looked around for her, looked in the deck-house. She was not there. Then he heard her soft flute music from the front of the barge. It seemed to tremble — it was more than sad, it was afraid. He listened for a moment, then started forward. The bristling spears stopped him on one side, so he took the other. He found her sitting with her back to the deck-house. The flute notes were single and did not touch each other. Each seemed unbearably sad, and caught in each was that trembling fear. He sat down by her side and waited till she put her flute in her lap. She was the strangest girl he had ever known — stranger than Susan, and *she* was hard enough to understand. But Soona, with her darkness, her still face, her deep eyes, seemed to have some secret that could not be shared, something from the air and soil and stone and mountains of O. She was, he thought, as strange as Chinese must have been to the first men from the west, as strange as Tibetans.

'Are you all right?'

'Yes. How is the boy?'

'He'll survive. We'll put him ashore on an island.'

'No, no.' Her vehemence startled him. She caught his wrist with fingers hard and strong — she was a fishergirl and had spent her life weaving nets. 'We must keep him. Keep him with us.'

'I don't see why. We'll have to guard him.'

'It doesn't matter. Nick, you must let me decide. There is a knowledge I carry. Do not ask. I carry it but don't know what it means. Susan will tell me. And tell you.'

'Sure,' Nick said. He did not like this — especially he did not want the Hotlander boy on the barge. He would never trust him. He had felt that arm jumping in its passion to kill. 'Why does he hate you? Why did he go at you like that?'

Soona relaxed, but kept her hand on his arm. She seemed to need the comfort of touching him. 'He carries knowledge too. It must be that. He does not know it — less than I. But he recognized me. He saw me and knew. And tried to kill me.'

'Why?'

'I am an enemy. I will do something terrible to him. And he to me. And both of us to all Humankind. He tried to kill me to save himself.'

'It doesn't make sense.'

'No, it doesn't.' She looked at him and smiled. Suddenly she leaned forward and kissed him. 'I like you, Nick. And I like Jimmy Jaspers. And I love Susan. But above all I love O.'

'Still doesn't make much sense,' he mumbled. He felt himself blushing, but wished that she would kiss him again. She let his hand go.

'Listen, Nick. There's an old song that's come back to me. I used to sing it in Stonehaven as I mended nets. I learned it from my mother and she from hers. No one knew how old it was or who made the words.' She played a few notes on her flute. Then she sang:

> 'One is red and one is white
> And they must go together.
> Hand in hand with one who knows
> They must go together.
>
> In the night and in the dawn,
> Fierce is one and gentle one,
> In the dying and the birthing
> They must go together.'

'Yes,' Nick said, 'I see.'

'Do you?'

'I'm not dumb. You're white. He's red. You're gentle and

105

he's fierce. I don't get the rest of it. Is Susan supposed to be the one who knows?' He was jealous that they must go hand in hand. 'And what's all this about night and dawn? And dying and birthing?'

'I don't know. It's only an old song.'

'You don't believe that.'

'All I know is, the Hotlander – the red one – recognized me. We're strangers, but he knew, something spoke in him. It spoke in me. What the rest is we'll learn in Furthermost.'

'If we find it.'

The first island was astern. Others lay on the left and right, and stretched ahead as far as Nick could see. He got up and went to the rail. 'Seafolk,' he called, 'do you know where Furthermost is?'

One of the seals, swimming with his head above the water, croaked in answer, 'We know.'

'Is Susan there?'

'She is there. And her friend, Thief.'

'Thief? Who's he?' But the seal was gone.

'Too many questions, Nick,' Soona said. 'We'll know in good time.' She raised her flute and played a happier tune. He listened a while, then turned to leave.

'Nick,' she said.

'Yes?'

'Guard him when he wakes. He will try to kill me.'

'We'll guard him.'

'Guard me too. If I grow afraid I will kill him.'

He went back to the stern. Jimmy and Dawn had shifted the Hotlander into the deck-house. He lay covered to his chin, with his head on a pillow of blankets. His cheeks had stopped twitching. He seemed no more than a boy in face-paint. If he scrubbed it off and let his hair grow he would be just a skinny kid.

'Soona says we've got to keep him.' The red one. The fierce

106

one. He hoped that Susan would have answers. He went outside and spent the rest of the afternoon digging spears from the deck-house with his knife. He gave them to Silverwing and Yellowclaw to make into arrows.

The Seafolk kept the barge moving till nightfall. They beached it on an island and swam off to a reef to sleep till dawn. But their leader, a big old seal with grey fur and a voice like a saw, stayed with the band. His name, he said, was Watcher of Furthermost. He had watched all his life, hoping that in his time none would need to go there. But word had come that Humankind had made the Weapon, so he and his tribe had stolen a barge from a river town and waited at the appointed place for the legendary 'One who knows'. Susan Ferris came. It seemed that she was woven into the history of O.

'We carried her to Furthermost on the barge. Then she told us to return for you.'

'And Thief was with her?' Nick said.

'Oh yes. Thief.'

'Who's he?'

'A creature we had thought none could befriend. But while he stays with her she need not fear. Unless these painted warriors track her down.'

Yellowclaw spoke from the far side of the fire. 'How can we reach this Furthermost tomorrow? The circle of islands is too wide.'

'Ah,' Watcher said, 'Freeman Wells chose the name to deceive. He wished to hide his island. But you are friends, so I will tell you. Furthermost is not furthermost from shore. The islands are a circle, as you say, and Futhermost is furthest from the rim.'

'In the centre?'

'That is it.'

'Clever sods,' Jimmy said.

107

'Just so,' said the seal. 'But I must go and eat some weed. These sounds of yours are spike-fish in my throat.' He heaved himself down the beach and swam away.

'I'll say this for Susie, she gets around,' Jimmy said.

Nick thought of her woven into O. Even though he would see her tomorrow she seemed far away, and strange to him, like a figure in a tapestry, from another time. He looked at the Varg ambling on the beach, with their fur shining silver-blue in the moonlight, and the Birdfolk in the shadows beyond the fire, great coloured eagles with faces half-human and half-bird, and he shivered and thought, What am I doing here? Soona played her flute. He wished she would play a tune he recognized.

Later Dawn went to the barge to look at the Hotlander. She left Bess guarding the deck-house door. Ben would take his turn later on.

'How is he?' Soona said.

'Waking, but I made him sleep again. His wounds will heal.'

'What are we going to call him?' Jimmy said.

'He has a name. He told me in his fever. He is Aenlocht of the Clohna tribe. He comes from the iron desert beyond a mountain that pours hot blood from the heart of O.'

'Lava,' Nick said.

'With Bess to help I looked into his mind, I questioned him. Osro's army is ready to march. He has warriors as numerous as the grains of sand. He has the fire weapon that eats up men and trees and stone. Aenlocht calls him Lord of Fire. He will take his army south, into the lands of darkness, but in his holy fire darkness will flee. The Hotlanders will enslave all living things – humans and Woodlanders, Birdfolk, and Seafolk and Varg. Enslave or kill. Osro will rule, and the tribes will be his spear and shield.'

'Does he know the Freemen are making the Weapon too?'

'He said nothing about that. He came south with a scouting party. They saw us and attacked.'

'Did you ask about Soona?'

'I tried. But I found only darkness and disorder. And dreadful fear. He knows who Soona is and does not know. He must kill her, that is all. She is enemy.'

'We gunner have ter keep an eye on him,' Jimmy said.

'He will sleep the rest of the night. Tomorrow his fever will be gone. But his wounds will not heal for many days. And what is in his mind may never heal.'

They lay down to sleep. Once Nick woke and saw the Varg change guard. Jimmy snored, and Soona, mysterious, slept with moonlight on her face, and sighed and seemed to fight some battle with herself. Down by the water frogs were croaking.

In the morning the Seafolk launched the barge with only Dawn and Jimmy and the Hotlander on board. To make it lighter, Nick and Soona walked with the Varg. The island was a large one, growing trees similar to silver birch and pine. Green and pink lichens crusted the rocks. Little bushes growing at knee-height were laden with blue berries sweet as jam. Nick and Soona picked some for Dawn and Jimmy. And once they found a Shy, growing by itself in a little hollow. The even-shaped bush and the pale blue flower were disappointing. But Nick remembered how Shy had saved him from Steen, and he brought a handful of water from a spring and poured it on the roots before going on. They waited on a rock at the tip of the island and jumped on the barge as it went by.

The islands were smaller after that and they had no chance to walk again. The Birdfolk had flown ahead to find Susan. Jimmy loafed on the deck-house roof. Aenlocht was still sleeping, held in the web of Dawn's medicine. Soona looked in at the door now and then, and came away with her eyes grown darker. The Varg swam, or loped over islands, keeping up easily with the barge. They reminded Nick of puppies playing games.

At midday Silverwing and Yellowclaw flew over the barge.

'Susan is waiting. We are going to see how close the armies have come to each other. Our thanks to you, Seafolk. Fare you well.' They flew on and soon went out of sight.

The islands were gathered close about and the barge seemed landlocked. But always channels opened, ways cut through. Nick began to watch ahead for Susan. All the islands were low and smooth – glaciated, Nick told himself – and grew only single trees or single copses, berry bushes, tufts of grass. It seemed an unlikely place for Freeman Wells to have made his home. Watcher of Furthermost raised his head. 'There,' he croaked.

The island was no different from the rest. Rocks pink and grey, berry patch, a stand of silver trees. Beside them, smooth-topped bed-rock rose in a hump.

Suddenly, he saw Susan. She came from the trees and walked to the water. She was wearing her Earth T shirt and shorts. He waved and yelled her name. She waved back. And then a Bloodcat ran from the hump of stone and charged towards her. It came like a red flash down the island, cleared the berry patch in a leap. Nick was yelling, the hairs on his head were standing up. Jimmy came lurching into the bow with his axe. But Soona said, 'It's all right. It must be Thief.'

The Bloodcat stopped at Susan's side. She dropped her hand on its neck easily. She raised her other hand and waved again.

'Nick. Jimmy. Soona,' she cried.

CHAPTER EIGHT

The Speaking Stone

He could not get used to the creature prowling round them as they ate. It went in a half circle, and turned and went back the other way, glaring at them, never blinking. The Varg watched it closely – one always watched. They understood, Dawn said, how shallow its control of itself was. The savagery underneath could break through at one wrong movement or wrong word. Only Susan was not afraid.

'He's not going to hurt you. He's not used to people, that's all.' She told them how Thief had saved her from Slarda. 'He knows you're my friends. I've told him about you. He won't come close but he won't attack. Just don't try to touch him, that's all.'

'He reminds me of Aenlocht.'

They told her about the Hotlander boy. A strange smile came on her face. 'It all fits in.'

'Fits in with what?'

'There's an old story, Nick, about three people.'

'And a song,' Soona said.

'Lots of songs. Freeman Wells told me the words.'

'Told?'

'He left his voice for me in the house.'

'What house?'

'I guess we're still a bit mixed up, young Susie,' Jimmie said.

'I'll show you soon. But the story says One who knows – that's me – '

'Knows what?'

'I'm not sure. I'll find out. And One who carries beauty. The Pale One – '

'That's Soona.'

'Soona and her flute. Did you bring it, Soona?'

'Yes,' whispered the girl.

'And One who carries fire in his mind. He's the Red One. That must be the Hotlander boy.'

'He's got a streak of lightning on his chest.'

'Yer could boil spuds on what 'e keeps in here.' Jimmy tapped his forehead.

'So it fits. I knew someone like him would come. I didn't know who. I thought for a while Thief might be the Red One. But it had to be someone human of course.'

'I don't understand all this,' Nick said. 'Can't we just go home?'

'No,' Susan said. 'No, we can't.'

'Tough luck, son,' Jimmy said.

'Well, what do these stories mean? And what do we do?'

'What do *I* do. And Soona. And the Hotlander boy.'

'You're not going anywhere without me.'

Thief hissed and stepped towards him.

'Don't talk so loudly, Nick,' Susan said. She took his hand. 'You're coming, wherever we go. Jimmy too, and Dawn. We'll go together. But in the end it's me and Soona and Aenlocht.'

'Doing what?'

She shrugged. 'I've got to meet Aenlocht first. Is he on the boat?'

'He's awake,' Dawn said. 'His mind is clear. But his wounds will be several days healing.'

'Can he walk? I want to take him into the house.'

'Nick and Jimmy must carry him.'

Susan nodded. 'Soona, you and I will make him ready.'

'He wants to kill Soona.'

'We'll take Thief. They're enemies and they've got to get used to each other.'

She stood up and walked to one side and Thief slunk forward and stood with her. 'Now, Soona.'

The fishergirl went towards them. Thief growled and the hair stood up along his back.

'Don't be frightened. Keep on the other side of me.'

'Susan, can I play a tune for him?'

'Yes, play.'

Soona lifted her flute. She moved carefully round to face Thief, and played a tune that spoke of ease, of comfort, calm of mind, acceptance of all things – that at least was how it seemed to Nick. At the end his hand was resting on Ben's neck. It did not work quite so well for Thief, but at last his rumbling stopped and the hairs on his back lay flat. Soona kept on a little while, and in the end he yawned and looked indifferently at her. He rubbed himself against Susan's leg.

Soona stopped. She slipped her flute into her sleeve. 'There,' she said, 'better than I thought. Distant friends.'

They went down to the beach and approached the barge. The old seal, Watcher of Furthermost, was by the stern. 'Susan, we will rest on the neighbouring island. Call when you need us again.'

'Thank you,' Susan said. 'We'll have to hear what Freeman Wells says first. Rest well, Watcher.'

She and Soona climbed on to the barge, and Thief came up with an easy leap. They stood on the deck and looked at the cabin. Thief took a step towards it. A soft anticipatory wicked hiss came from his mouth. But Susan said, 'Thief, no! Listen to me, Thief.'

She 'spoke' to him, and she had learned a kind of shorthand now. An image of her hand on his head meant *stay*, an image of her standing with someone else meant *do not attack.* She could not be sure he would always obey, but in some way he wished to please her; he allowed her things, but took no orders. If his instinct to attack overrode their friendship then she would have no influence with him.

She tried to show herself and the Hotlander boy. She had not seen him and it was hard. But she found the image in her mind reinforced – colour and precision added to it, features she could not know about; and she sent a startled glance at Soona. The fishergirl was 'speaking' too. Somehow their minds had joined, had woven round each other like two vines. In her wonder at the strangeness, she almost lost Thief. The Bloodcat took two steps to the deck-house door, and paused, and crouched. From inside came a cry of rage and fear. Aenlocht thought they had sent the cat to kill him. But they made their image again – combining with an ease neither stopped to question – and made the animal stay, they held him by the force of their need. Without this boy O would be destroyed. Then Susan went forward and looked in the door.

Aenlocht had thrown his blanket off. That was all he had strength for. He bared his teeth and snarled like the cat. He would fight with fingernails and teeth – for the moment it would take Thief to kill him. But in savagery he was the Bloodcat's equal.

'Thief, Thief,' she said; and held the cat. She stepped into the doorway and turned her back on Aenlocht. She felt Soona's mind increasing her own, and again presented Aenlocht as friend – while behind her the boy hissed and spat.

Thief tried to force her out of the way. He did it with care. She sensed that, behind her, Aenlocht was looking on with disbelief. No one treated Bloodcats in this way. She held the door-jamb with two hands, resisting his

114

pressure. He could so easily knock her aside. 'No, Thief.'
Then to Soona, 'Play your flute. Show him O.'

At once the music came. Soona understood. Streams
running on pebbles, pools deep and green, ferny grottoes,
bracken slopes warm in the afternoon sun; giant trees,
deserts red and hot, caves and mountains, green swelling
seas bursting on reefs – and the vast sweep of yellow plains,
and blue jungle, blue hills, with curtains of shifting rain:
all was there, the music held it all. And Susan understood
that for the first time in his life Thief the Bloodcat saw O
in colour. He trembled, seemed to lose the use of his legs,
and sank on his belly. He gave little growls and mews of
wonder; and in the cabin the Hotlander boy made the same
sounds. The music had entered him.

Then suddenly, like a crushing of the mind, colour went
out. The music changed – and Soona's face, as she played,
was white with the horror of what she was doing. O became
a grey world, dead and dry. The hills were piles of ash, the
jungles dead, and deserts grey, and streams gone dry. The
seas lay still and seemed to rot. Susan wailed with grief, and
the Bloodcat howled, and Aenlocht howled; and tears ran
on Soona's cheeks. She did not stop. She played until the
horror of it put out all their sounds – and then, only then,
let a little thread of colour in. It trickled in the grey deserts
like water, it curled through the dead soil like a root. They
held their breath: this was life. Then Soona let a river flow,
she let a green tree heave up its head in the wind. It swayed
and sang. And Susan found her mind in the music too,
helping to make it. And the three, Susan, Soona, Aenlocht,
with Thief at their side, stood under the tree and held up
their hands, and with the flat of their palms pushed death
back, turned back the grey, and made colour stand in O
again. The fight was hard. Pain was in all of them at the
hardness of it. Death and evil beat on them, grey winds,

and tried to rip the courage from their minds. But they stood, they held it off with the flat pressure of their hands. And so it went on – and would go on . . . but Soona stopped. She came to an end, and with a little sob lowered her flute, and stood swaying on the deck of the barge. Susan stumbled to her, held her in her arms.

'Who played, Soona? Who?'

'I don't know. I began it. Then something came in and took it away. It played with me – it made the colour, and the grey, and showed us all together. You and me, and him – and Thief too.'

Susan looked at the door. The Hotlander boy had crawled from his bed and lay against the jamb, supporting himself. Thief was by his side. Neither seemed aware of the other.

Soona said, 'Whatever we must do, it is dreadful harm. A necessary harm. And greater good.'

'Yes,' Susan said. 'Now we'd better listen to Freeman Wells.'

The others, Jimmy and Nick and Dawn and the Varg, were standing by the prow of the barge. They too had heard the music. They helped the girls down, and Jimmy and Nick climbed into the barge and made a sling of blankets and carried Aenlocht to the side and lowered him on to the beach. Thief had gone to Susan. He stood between her and Soona, and both of them had a hand on his neck. There were no more questions about friendship. Not with the Bloodcat or the boy. The music had shown them how it was.

Nick, on the outside, could not argue. He knew his use was to give what help was asked; and so he made the sling again and carried Aenlocht up the island. Jimmy was, for Jimmy, very quiet. The Varg walked with a ponderous gait. Dawn kept by Aenlocht's side, watching his wounds, frightened they might open. At the mound of glaciated stone Nick and Jimmy put him down.

Susan said, 'This is Freeman Wells' house. Watcher showed me how to open the door.' She put her palm on the rock as if to feel its warmth, and murmured something, and a slab swung away on hinges, revealing a square room. 'Open Sesame,' Nick said, and Susan grinned at him. She stepped inside and touched another wall, murmured again. A second door opened. 'Come in. There's room for everyone.'

They stepped into the ante-room and the door closed behind them. Susan and Thief and Soona went ahead, down wide stone stairs into a larger room. It was lit by lamps glowing on the walls. The air was sweet and cool. Jimmy and Nick laid Aenlocht on a couch against a wall. His eyes darted about – for an outdoor being, a nomad, this descent into stone must be terrifying. Yet he made no sound. Dawn tried to touch the wound on his shoulder but he put up his hand and kept her away. He watched while Susan closed the inner door. They were all inside, Ben and Bess too, yet the room was not crowded. Doors opened off into sleeping chambers and workrooms and a kitchen; and, Nick supposed, some sort of bathroom and lavatory. The couches against the walls had woven covers. The chairs and the long oval table in the centre were stone – but stone made light, carved and turned like wood. Everything was simple and comfortable, and Susan seemed very much at home here.

Jimmy looked around. 'Some place. It'd take some makin'.'

'Yes,' she said.

'How'd he do it?'

'I don't know. Freeman Wells – I think he was the greatest person who ever lived. He wasn't a scientist, or a magician. He made magic a science and science magic. He saw more than anyone had seen. And understood it.'

117

'It didn' stop 'im gettin' 'is neck busted,' Jimmy said.

'No, it didn't. He was just human, like you and me. But as well as seeing what had been, and is, he saw what might be. So, in a way, he's still alive.'

'Don't go makin' too much of him, Susie.'

'I don't. He's done his part. There's nothing he can do any more. It's up to us.'

'Susan, you must tell us,' Soona said. It was plain she meant her and Aenlocht. The others did not exist for her now. She walked across the room and sat on the couch by the Hotlander boy. He shifted and made room.

'Yes,' Susan said. She went into a workroom and came back with a plaited basket, which she put on the table. She opened it and set the lid on one side.

'There are several things in here. Some I haven't touched yet. I can only take them out with Soona and Aenlocht. This one though' – she lifted out a white stone, polished smooth. It filled her palm. Nick saw traceries of blue and silver, like veins of precious metal – 'this one is for all of us. Freeman Wells made it a long time ago, more than a hundred and thirty turns.'

'Before the Halfmen?' Nick whispered.

'Yes, before that. Do you all know the story of Freeman Wells and Otis Claw? How Otis Claw stole the Halves from the Motherstone and humans became only half. They were good or evil, and evil won. But Freeman Wells took the Halves from Otis Claw. In his hall. And made a dome of light about the Motherstone. What Nick would call a force field. And then his strength was gone. They hunted him. He hid the Halves and came to Earth, and found me. He put the Mark on me – ' she showed her wrist – 'and then they captured him, and killed him, the Halfmen. And they found Jimmy and used him to capture me and send me to O.'

'Yeah,' Jimmy said, 'what a bloddy no-hoper I was.'

'But Nick and I, and Jimmy too, we found the Halves where Freeman Wells had left them, and put them back on the Motherstone – '

'It wasn't that easy,' Nick said. 'And it was you.'

' – and humans were whole again.'

'Didn' do no good. They give it all away to them priests.'

'Yes,' Susan said, 'but that's over.'

'Tell us what to do,' Soona said.

'Freeman Wells will tell you. In the days before the Halfmen, when Otis Claw was Otis Hand and O was happy, Freeman Wells came to Furthermost with Marna, his wife, and they made this house, and Freeman Wells lived here and made – science magic, and magic science.'

'Tell us.'

'Yes.' The eyes of the fishergirl and the Hotlander boy were fixed on her. The Pale One and the Red One, she thought. How clever he was to know, and how right it is. She smiled at them, then looked at the stone. The veins of blue and silver grew bright. 'Freeman Wells,' she said, 'speak again. Let everyone hear.'

For a moment there was silence. Nick seemed to hear the thump of his blood, he heard the sound of Jimmy scratching his jaw, and a soft mew of anticipation from Thief. Then the air in the room began to hum. The voice, when it spoke, did not come from the stone, it came from all around them. It croaked and lurched, like the voice from someone waking from a long sleep.

'If you hold the stone, you are One who knows, you are the Knower. If you hear my voice, the last days are come.'

'A cheerful bogger,' Jimmy said.

The voice grew more even and came with a faint echo in the room. 'There is no mystery in my knowing. There are ways. And last is a fearful word, but words can change.

119

And times with them. There is a path. It is a hard one. But last can be changed into first, if all is right.'

' 'e takes 'is time gettin' to the point,' Jimmy said.

'Shsh, Jimmy.'

'Listen! Here is what I have found. The fire that consumes the world. The fire that eats up stone, that swallows O. I have made it – and shall unmake. I shall tear all knowledge of it from my brain, I shall carry all the work of my hands to the deepest place and bury it, and no one will ever find it again. I shall do that. But – what I cannot do is tear it from the brains of those who follow. I cannot. And one day some clever human will find it – and then, be he good or evil, the last days are come.

'Listen again! Because the fire destroys, humans will destroy. That is their nature – to increase, to dominate, to be master. Destruction follows. In their present shape, that is the law governing Humankind. I see the means to change it, but these are not last days – these days I speak in – and I have not the right. Yours is the right.

'Listen. I will tell you about the fire . . . What it touches, it consumes. In itself it is not evil, it is simply fire refined to its purest state. But of its nature it does certain things. I need not tell them. Only this – that when it meets itself it meets a foe, and the foe is equal, and the battle between them never stops until the thing that feeds them is consumed.'

Soona had begun to sway. 'O feeds them,' she whispered. Aenlocht locked his hand on hers.

'Humans control the fire when it is one,' Freeman Wells went on. 'They turn it on and off like a tap – even though the smoke of the burning poisons the air, and in time will poison O. But when two meet – and there will be two, where one Weapon is another will follow – and fire fights fire, then they are no longer Humankind's to control.

Humans are nothing. The Weapons have no master, but fight and feed, unstoppable. And did I hear the Pale One say, they feed on O? That is the truth. You have heard old songs and prophecies. O is a cinder, turning in space. The fire has eaten her. All is dead.'

Thief was whimpering softly. He had sunk down by Susan's legs and lay against them for what comfort he could find. The Varg were moaning. They swayed in unison, in a grieving for their planet, for their kind. Soona wept silently. But Susan stood straight, holding the stone. Her face was pinched and stern.

'There's more,' she said. 'We're waiting, Freeman Wells.'

'That is the first thing,' said the voice. 'Now I will tell you a second. I hear the question. You have a question in your minds. Can the makers of this Weapon not be told? The answer is yes. They can be. They must be. They have made it, now they must be told what it is.'

'Then they'll stop,' Nick cried. 'They'll destroy it the way you did.' But as he spoke he remembered Osro, and remembered the fat councillor and the thin one, who controlled Kenno.

'And then they'll stop! I hear you say it. I cannot see, I do not know who has come with the Knower, and the Pale One, and the Red One. But I can hear that one cries, "They will stop!" Well . . . it must be tried. You must go and tell them. Perhaps, perhaps . . . And it will give you something to keep you busy. Try. And hope. But do not hope too hard. Man is man.'

'Get to the bloddy point,' Jimmy snarled. 'We know we're ratbags.'

The stone was silent. Then it spoke, the air spoke, in a voice uncompromising, hard – yet grieving too, and mortified. 'Let me speak about Humankind. About *us*. We are new. Of all the kinds of O, the thinking kinds –

Woodlanders and Stonefolk, Birdfolk and Seafolk, and Varg too – humans are newest. The origins were one, but the ways were many, and the times of starting various. Humans came last – but they made up for it. Theirs was a headlong rush through the tale of kinds. The others – they stopped and rested, they came to places where nature cried, "Enough!" – and there they stayed through millenia, through aeons, and when they were firm in that place, they moved on. And so today they are what they should be – harmonious beings. Not so humans. Not so Humankind. We are discordant. I cannot say what we are. We travelled too fast – we made no rest – gave ourselves no time. The swamp is in us still. The swamp beast overcomes us, and when we should think we bellow, we strike and tear – and so fall back into that dark place where self is all. And the thinking, loving half can make no sound. Yes, it is there. But cannot speak. For we are out of balance, and the Halves on the Motherstone, equal once, weigh differently. Fault not in their making, but in us.'

The voice said no more for a time, and spoke tiredly when it spoke again. 'Yes, go and tell them. They must know. There is one who thinks locked in with the swamp beast. Let them confront each other. The chance is worth taking. But now I must speak to those who travel another way. To the Knower, and the Pale One, and the Red One. What I have to say is for them alone. And I promise nothing easy.'

The stone in Susan's hand seemed to die, the veins of colour went out.

' 'e's a cheerful sod,' Jimmy said.

'He tells the truth.'

'It ain't the sort of truth I like ter hear. There's nothin' I can get me meathooks on. Fightin' with bloddy shadders is no fight.'

'Jimmy, please. Go outside. Nick, you too. I'm sorry, but

122

you heard him. Dawn, you can't stay. I wish you could. But it's only for the three of us to hear.'

'And Thief?' Nick said.

'Yes, him. He won't leave us.'

'Will you tell us what he says?'

'If I can.' She went to the stone wall and put her hands on it and the door swung open. Nick and Jimmy and Dawn and the Varg climbed the stairs to the ante-room. Susan slipped by, with Thief at her side, and opened the door to the island. Nick stopped beside her. 'How long will you be?'

'I don't know. As long as he takes.'

He looked back into the larger room and saw Soona sitting on the couch with Aenlocht. Their hands were still clasped. He felt jealous, and said, 'I always get left out.'

'No you don't, Nick. You brought them here. That was an important thing.' She put her hand on his arm and Thief growled. 'You're making him jealous now. Go on. I'll tell you what happens – if I can.'

'Yeah. Good luck.' He stepped into the open and the door closed with a sleek sound. He could not see the place where the joins were made. The smooth mound rose as high as a house. Dawn and the Varg had climbed to the top and Jimmy was going up, using his axe as a walking stick. Nick scrambled after him.

'I don't like it.'

'Nor do I. But there's nothin' ter do.'

'What do you think he's telling them?'

'Somethin' bloody dangerous, that's fer sure.'

They sat down with the bears and the Woodlander girl and the afternoon passed. The islands lay all about, locking Furthermost in. The barge on the beach was clear of the water, but the tide did not rise and fall much here. On the nearest island the Seafolk slept in the sun.

'How long?' Nick said.

'It's like waitin' fer a baby ter get born.'

'Were you ever married, Jimmy?'

'Yeah, once. Had a good wife. And a kid. But I treated 'em bad. So she up an' left. Can't say I blame her. I hope they're doin' O.K., wherever they are.'

'Do you miss Earth?'

Jimmy shrugged. 'Sometimes. I'd like a jug of beer. An' a feed of fish an' chips. I'd like ter have an afternoon at the races. Never had much luck with the gee-gees though.' He thought a while. 'No, I don't miss it. Ole Ben here, he's the best mate I ever had.'

The Varg nodded wisely.

'What about you, Dawn? We could use the Shy and get you to Earth.'

'No.' She shook her head. 'I cannot run. And outside of Wildwood I would die.'

'Woodlanders didn't make the Weapon. Do you hate humans?'

She thought about that and did not answer him directly. 'Freeman Wells was human. Soona and Aenlocht are human. And Susan, and you, though you come from another world. All I know is – if O dies Humankind have killed her. And if she lives, Humankind save her.'

Nick thought she was being too generous. He lay on the sun-warmed rock and tried to sleep, but his mind would not let him. Down there, in the room of stone, Freeman Wells was telling Susan – the Knower, he thought, with a sneer – and the Pale One, and the Red One, what to do. But he could not be disdainful for long. The importance of it kept on flooding through him. He banged his fist softly on the stone. 'Hurry up,' he whispered.

'Look,' Dawn said, 'over there.' She was pointing eastwards over the islands. He peered but could see nothing.

'Silverwing and Yellowclaw.' He made out distant spots on the sky. 'And two more. Warrior Birds.'

They came in low and fast. Nick and Dawn and Jimmy climbed off the mound and met them on the grass by the beach.

'Where is Susan?'

'She's in the house talking to Freeman Wells.'

'Listenin',' Jimmy growled. 'No one else can get a word in.'

'We have flown over Osro's army,' Yellowclaw said. 'And these Warriors of Morninghall come from the south. Sundercloud and Snowflier are their names. They have watched Kenno's army gather. He moves north, Osro south. Each has the Weapon. Osro has it mounted on a sled which Hotlanders pull – '

'And the Freemen have theirs on a giant cart,' Sundercloud said. 'Oxen pull it. There are five wheels on each side, each as tall as a man. The Weapon is a monstrous machine of wood and iron. It has a snout that spits out yellow fire, straight as a bowstring. They try it on the cliffs and trees and streams. It eats them all. And smoke boils up and poisons the sky.'

'And the same with Osro. He tries his machine. It melts and boils, devours, and nothing is left. We took boulders, Silverwing and I, and dropped them to smash this evil thing, but he has a roof of iron built over it, sloping steep, and our boulders bounced away and did no harm. We cannot fight it. He turned the snout into the sky and tried to burn us. It moves slowly, otherwise we would not be here.'

'What can be done?' Sundercloud said.

'We must ask Susan.'

'She's still inside,' Nick said. 'But Freeman Wells told us about the Weapon. If two are made, and they fight, they start a chain reaction that burns up O. It'll be a cinder. Everything dead. That's what he said.'

'And even without that,' Dawn said, 'the smoke from one will poison all of O. Nothing will live.'

'That's the message,' Jimmy said. 'So we better hope the second part sounds good.'

'But that's not all,' Nick cried. 'I've got to talk to Osro and Kenno. He said it was worth trying.'

'He said it would keep yer busy, that's what he said. It's likely ter be the last thing yer ever do. This Osro geezer will see ter that.'

'I've got to try.'

'How will yer get there?'

'The Birdfolk will take me. Yellowclaw, you can carry me. I know I'm heavy. But we can make a sling and two of you can lift it.'

'It can be done. But it will be dangerous. Jimmy's right. Osro will try to kill you.'

'An' maybe Kenno too, if his mates 'ave a say.'

'Yes,' Nick said, 'but all the same ... '

They made their plans. Nick would leave in the morning with the three Warrior Birds. Silverwing would stay with the others as messenger.

'Now, this sling. There's plenty of stuff in the house.'

'How do we get in, knock at the door?' Jimmy said.

They looked at the mound of stone. As if she had been waiting, Susan walked out. She came alone, leaving the door open. She walked very straight, though her face was stricken with some kind of grief. She had been told; and it had been almost too much for her. Nick saw the effort she made to walk down steadily through the blueberries.

'Susan? Where's Thief?'

'He's with Soona and Aenlocht. He's friends with all three of us now.'

'What happened, Susan?'

'Freeman Wells told us what to do.'

'What? What is it?'

'I can't tell you. I can't talk. I'm so tired. I've got to sleep. I've got to go back into the house and sleep.' She was whispering. They barely heard her voice. 'I came to say, tomorrow we leave. Please get ready. Tell the Seafolk.'

'Where are we going?'

She swayed and he jumped to hold her up. 'Where, Susan?'

'To the Motherstone. Me and Soona and Aenlocht. And Thief. To the Motherstone.'

CHAPTER NINE

Face to Face

The barge was ready and the house was closed. The stone mound grew pink in the dawn light. Jimmy and Dawn were already aboard, and Silverwing turned overhead, with her feathers shining. Aenloch and Soona came to the beach side by side. The boy moved slowly. Soona helped, an arm about his waist. Her black hair was braided and hung to her waist. They looked like Red Indians, Nick thought. He stepped forward to say goodbye. Aenloch bared his teeth, he held up his hand with fingers clawed. 'Stay back, Nick,' Susan whispered. Soona smiled at him – a tiny smile – and passed on. He wasn't sure she knew who he was. Jimmy helped them into the barge.

Thief was at Susan's side. He too bared his teeth when Nick went close.

'You know where to meet us?' Susan said.

'Yes. In two days.'

'Good luck, Nick.'

'You don't think it'll do any good. None of you do.'

'He said you had to try.' She put her hand on his arm and Thief growled.

'Tell your pet I knew you first.'

'Don't be jealous, Nick. When it's all finished we'll go home. Just the two of us.'

She went to the barge and climbed in. Thief jumped up beside her, and the Varg, their fur alight with blue and pink, heaved the barge into the open water, where the Seafolk guided it away. Susan did not wave. Jimmy waved. 'Take it easy, young feller.'

'I will, Jimmy.'

He watched until the barge went from sight behind an island. Then he walked to the three Warrior Birds at the end of the beach. Yellowclaw had his wings raised to Silverwing, circling over the barge. He sighed and lowered them and turned to Nick. 'It is always goodbye. And never any certainty of meeting.'

'No,' Nick said. 'Where are we going first?'

'To Osro. It will take all day to get there. Then south to Kenno's army tomorrow.'

'How will I talk to Osro?'

'In the night. That's the only safe way.'

They laid out the sling of knotted cloths he and Dawn had made, he wrapped himself in a cloak taken from the house, and sat in the centre. Yellowclaw and Sundercloud took the stick handles and leaped and beat their wings and lifted Nick clear of the island. He saw the barge again. It seemed to have gone no distance at all. It looked like a toy boat in a ditch. Susan and Dawn and Soona stood in the stern. They all waved. That was better. Thief was a splash of red on the deck-house roof. He saw Ben and Bess walking on the shore. Jimmy shook his axe. They went on south, and the Birdfolk flew east, gaining height. Soon the two groups lost sight of each other.

Nick was glad of the cloak. The beat of wings over him made a gale. He pulled it over his head and about his ears. The Birdfolk would climb and then approach the coast in a long glide. That way they would save their strength.

The islands were spread out in a flat shield. North and south he soon made out the edges, and west the rim stopped short of the horizon. East though, they lapped the coast. They seemed like a shoal of creatures from the sea trying to invade it. There were thousands, all sizes, all shapes.

He would never be able to find Furthermost again. He did not know how the Birdfolk had managed to find it.

The mountains and the forests climbed back inland. South the cape where the whirlpool lay jutted like a club of knotted wood into the sea. He thought that south again, dimly, he made out Susan's island. He wasn't sure; and not sure that a faint line in the haze, threading south, was Sheercliff. But ahead, he made out the lake where the Hotlanders had camped, and jungles north of that – Susan must have crossed them with Thief – and a paleness, a haziness, far north that was probably desert. And somewhere inland, towards the south, was the river he had sailed down on his tree. He wasn't sure he wanted to see that again.

Yellowclaw and Sundercloud stopped climbing. They began their eastward glide and the sling dragged a little behind. Nick had a view of the two great Warrior Birds above him, and the rippling spread of their wings. At midday they crossed the coast. The reef where the Hotlanders had flung Aenlocht at the barge curved like a black claw in the sea. The lake ran inland, bent like a boomerang. They dropped in three long swoops and landed on a hilltop. The Birdfolk put the sling down and Nick jumped out and stretched his legs.

'No Hotlanders?'

'None close to us. We're safe here for a while.'

'Which way is Osro?'

'North and east. See there, he tests his Weapon.'

Far away over the forest, smoke boiled up. It was so thick it seemed solid, and seemed to increase from inside itself. It was bulbous, smooth, pus-yellow – it was cancerous, Nick thought. Soon it stood in a manshape a kilometre high, bending to the south, and heavy at the top, as though it

130

had a brain there and could think. Then its hard edge broke and smoke began to spread across the sky.

'Every day it is the same,' Yellowclaw said. 'They fill the sky with their poison and the wind spreads it over O. Look south, Kenno answers.'

A second tower rose, in colour, shape, solidity, identical with the first. It seemed to puff itself up with rage; with poison, like a swaying snake, Nick thought. Then it too broke. There were many kilometres between the armies, many days of marching, yet it was not long before the smoke of their weapons was carried by conflicting winds into each other. They ran together like puddles of water.

Nick turned away. He could not watch. He could not eat when Snowflier offered him food. He seemed to feel filth dropping on him. Humans were doing this to O.

Sundercloud had flown away to scout. At mid-afternoon he returned. 'They are camped on a plain at the edge of the forest. There is a hill close by where we can watch.'

Yellowclaw and Snowflier carried Nick. He lay face down and watched the jungle passing – rivers and gorges, hillsides, cliffs, chasms, trees like green puff-balls, black trees and brown. They went round to the north to avoid the smoke, and he saw the desert far away, with the steaming thermal waste of the Belt on its near side.

For the last part of the journey they flew low to avoid being seen against the sky. They skimmed down a valley and landed on a hill below the tree line. 'Through the trees,' Sundercloud said, 'the hill slopes down to the plain. There are rocks to hide us, and no scouts up here. But take care. Hotlanders have sharp eyes.'

Nick climbed to the top of the hill and over the brow. He went down among the trees into the boulders, and crept among them until the plain opened up. It was yellow grassland but seemed to have grown a garden of red and blue flowers. They bloomed to the edges of the hills: Hotlander tents, Hotlander weapon-stacks. The warriors, men and women, moved in the alleys like a multitude of ants. The size of the army made him gasp, but he had no time to marvel at it, for the Weapon, Osro's fire-gun, sat on its sledge by the largest tent, and once he had seen it he could not look away. It was squat and black, a pyramid with a flattened top. Its sides were plated with iron and a pagoda roof, spiked at the top, covered it like a lid. A dome rose from the pyramid, shining, silver, bald – a metal head; and from it poked an amputated snout, the gun itself. Nick shivered. His skin seemed to wither and turn dry.

Yellowclaw came to his side. 'An ugly sight. An abomination.'

'Yes,' Nick whispered.

'See, over there, where it has eaten.'

Nick looked along the line of hills at the south of the plain. One was bitten out. A crater smoked in its side. Another was gashed open, split like an apple. Melted stone shone like glass in the cleft. A third had a hole bored deep in its face, like a tunnel that a train might suddenly burst from.

'It goes through to the other side,' Yellowclaw said. 'As though a giant worm had burrowed there.'

'Osro's line of eaten hills stretches back to the desert,' Sundercloud said. 'Another comes to meet it from the Temple in the south.'

'There he is,' Snowflier said, 'standing by his tent. His face is like the carrion bird's, sitting on its feast.'

Nick could see only a group of figures. None stood out from the rest. He wished for eyes as sharp as the Birdfolk's, but shivered at the thought of seeing Osro again.

'They see us,' Yellowclaw said. 'They run to aim their Weapon. Climb on the boulder, Nick.'

He scrambled up, trying to watch the Weapon at the same time. Men were running to it. A door opened in its side and they climbed in. The Birdfolk had run free of the boulders. They leaped into the air, and Yellowclaw swung back for Nick. The silver head of the Weapon turned.

'Take my legs. Hold tight,' Yellowclaw cried. He hovered over Nick, his legs in reach, and Nick made a jump and locked his hands on them. Yellowclaw beat upwards at the same time and they rose and lumbered back over the hill, so low that Nick's feet trailed in the tops of trees. He had no chance to look at the Weapon again. Sundercloud and Snowflier were keeping parallel, and when the hill hid them the three Birdfolk turned and glided at an angle down its face. They came to the river and flew along its bed. Nick heard a gobbling, a hissing, a roar, and a vicious light flashed across his eyes.

'They have burned the top off the hill. Don't look, it will blind you.'

They flew on, the river turned, and turned again, and at last Yellowclaw put Nick down on the shingle. He landed beside him, heaving for breath.

'See. The smoke.' The monster towered, bulbous, yellow, hard. He seemed to lean to see them in the valley.

'Let's get out.'

'In a moment. We're safe here. That is the Weapon. You have seen it.'

'Osro won't give it up.'

'Do you still want to try?'

'Yes, I'll try. He might as well know what it is he's doing.'

'A man like Osro,' Yellowclaw said, 'might destroy a world out of malice. Or for his pleasure, even though it brings his own death too.'

That was more than Nick could understand. 'I'll talk to

him. I'll try and make him see. Hadn't we better go? The Hotlanders will be coming.'

They flew on down the river, with Nick in the sling. Dark was falling when they turned south, and it was night as they made a great sweep and came towards Osro's camp from the east. Fires were burning in front of the tents, spread out on the dark plain like stars in the sky. A huge fire, a mountain of fire, blazed by Osro's tent, lighting the red walls and blue roof, and the Weapon squatting on its sledge. The silver head and bare snout gleamed.

Warriors sat round the fires cooking their meal. The smell of roasting meat rose into the air, mixed with wood smoke. Sundercloud and Snowflier carried Nick. They began a smooth circling high over the central fire. Even at the height of a hundred metres, Nick felt the heat.

'Now,' Yellowclaw said, 'I will fetch out Osro.'

He half folded his wings and began a dive out towards the hills. Nick saw him sweep round, a dim shape, and angle back. He came in like a bat over the fire, and gave a great beat of his wings that sent him climbing out of the light, and sent a sheet of flame licking Osro's tent. The warriors yelled. Several hurled spears, but Yellowclaw was gone. His voice came booming from the dark.

'Osro! Come out, Osro. Listen to the message we have brought.'

Warriors hurled branches on the fire, making it flare, lighting Yellowclaw as he hung over the tent. But he was out of range and the Hotlanders did not waste their spears. Several ran to the Weapon and climbed in. Others turned a winch, sliding back a panel in the roof.

'Osro, come out.'

There was no movement from the tent, though warriors made a wall across the door.

'He's not going to come,' Snowflier said. 'A bowman could pick him off from here.'

Yellowclaw flew up. 'We must watch the Weapon. Nick, give your message. He will hear.'

Nick felt naked. He felt the heat of the fire on his face, and saw the light playing on the underside of the Birdfolk's wings. But he had the message rehearsed and he drew breath to begin; and was glad his voice had broken in the last year. It would be embarrassing to shout in a falsetto.

'Osro, I am Nicholas Quinn. Your hunters didn't kill me. Listen to the message. It comes from Freeman Wells.'

That brought Osro out. He came striding from the tent, broke through his guards, stood in the light, a tall figure, thin as a mantis, with spiky-looking limbs and crooked face and eyes that shone like hot points of light. Nick saw him standing clear for a moment, before his guards ran forward and hid him under a roof of shields.

'Osro, Freeman Wells found the Weapon. He found it more than a hundred turns ago. Before the time of the Halfmen. Before Otis Claw and the Priests of Ferris. He found it and destroyed it, because he understood what it would do.'

'Lies!' Osro shouted. 'There was no Freeman Wells. He was a myth, a tale for women. *I* made the Weapon. *I* am first.'

'Does it matter who was first? It's the same Weapon. He saw that it would destroy the whole world. Listen, Osro. You're a scientist. The smoke from the hills you burn is poisoning O. The trees are dying. The grass is sick. All the creeks and rivers are going bad. The fish will die. Everything will die. You can see it. Don't pretend you can't.'

Osro came breaking out of his guards. They sprang and covered him again. 'Lies, Earth-boy. Go back where you belong. Leave O to O. Leave O to me. The war will be

135

over before O is poisoned. And what do a few trees matter? And a few streams? Or a hundred streams? All the forests? It is a way of getting rid of the vermin who hide there. What matters is that Osro will rule O. And rule with the Weapon, and with the tribes. Do not come talking of trees and streams.'

The panel on the Weapon was open. The silver snout pointed up over the fire. But the Birdfolk had floated round to another quarter of the sky. Warriors spun a wheel to turn the pyramid, but it came at a creeping pace.

'All right,' Nick yelled, 'that's only the first part. Freeman Wells found out something else.'

'There was no Freeman Wells.'

'He lived. He made the Weapon. Listen, Osro. Just be a scientist for a few minutes, not a king. He saw that if one weapon fought with another, if the fires met, a chain reaction would start, men wouldn't be in control any more. The whole of O would be eaten up.'

'Lies! You try to frighten my tribes. Hotlanders do not frighten.'

'I'm telling you the truth. The Freeman army has the Weapon too. If you fight, that's the end.'

'My Weapon is better. I will strike first. Mine will destroy theirs.'

'Listen! Listen! Stop being mad and listen. It doesn't matter who strikes first. If one burns up the other, that's enough. You made the Weapon Osro, you can see it.' He knew that Osro understood, and believed that if he could only find the right words he would persuade him. 'You can stop it. You can save the world. You can be greater that way than by sitting on a throne.'

'He preaches! This boy! He preaches at me as though *I* were the child. Osro! King! This – this *nothing*, dares to look down on me from the sky and tell me how I may be great.'

136

'Osro, listen.'

'Go, boy. Go to your friends. Make *them* lay the Weapon down. And tell them Osro comes to be their king. Say to them, turn back, leave the Weapon where it stands. That way I may let them live. Otherwise my Weapon shall burn theirs.'

'But O will burn.'

'So be it. The planet shall not outlive its king.'

'You're mad, Osro. You're a maniac.'

'Burn him! Make him dust! Make him nothing!'

The great burning ray leapt out. It was silent, instantaneous, thrusting into the sky. But it was only a show of power. The Birdfolk were away, beating for the hills. Nick cried, 'Osro, stop. You'll kill the whole world,' but he heard how thin it was, the falsetto wail he had been afraid of; and he was silent, and watched the army shrink back into the dark, underneath the spear of light embedded in the sky. The Warrior Birds beat on and hills turned between them and Osro's camp.

They flew into the night. No one spoke. There was nothing to say. It was midnight before they stopped. Yellowclaw found a hollow by a stream on an upland plain. They made a small fire and warmed some food. 'We are halfway between the armies. This is where they will meet, on this plain.'

'When?'

'In four days. Five. Do you still want to talk to Kenno?'

'I've got to.'

'We'll reach him late in the morning. Rest, Nick – if you can. This is a day that will fill our dreams with hideous shapes.'

But Nick did not dream, he was too exhausted. Only, towards morning, things began to move in the shadows of his mind, he sensed their bulk but could not make out their

137

form – things huge and cumbersome and terrifying. He was glad he woke before they came into the light. He took off all his clothes and washed in the stream, though the shock of cold made him shout. He wondered how long it would be before this stream was poisoned. And he wondered how he and Susan could get to the cave and back to Earth before the battle – the last battle. There was no time.

In mid-morning, face down in the sling, he saw the river he had ridden down on his tree. The Birdfolk took him low. 'There is where we found you,' Yellowclaw cried. 'Lying on the stone, half dead, flashing your knife in the sun.'

It seemed long ago. He saw the water splashing in the gorge. The pillar of rock seemed no climb at all, and the line of red bushes an easy path. But it had not been so. It was just that now, in this danger to the whole of O, every other thing was shrunken.

They flew on over the forest, and far away he saw the sun flashing on the sea, turning it white. It seemed as empty as the sky. Somewhere out there Susan was making her way south to the Motherstone. What was the task she had to do there? He was frightened to guess. Whatever it was had almost been too much for her to bear learning about.

'There, on the river, Kenno's army,' Yellowclaw cried.

It was crossing a ford. The green river turned yellow downstream. The Weapon-cart was halfway over, with water foaming against the wheels. The oxen strained and bellowed – a team of twenty – whips cracked, men leaned their shoulders to the wheels, others hauled on ropes, and slowly, slowly, the cart made the crossing, turning its nose slightly to the current. The Weapon sat with the weight of lead. It was less fearsome-looking than Osro's. It was like a fort of logs, with here and there a plating of polished ox-hide fastened with rivets. On top was a pill-box, a truncated cone. But the nozzle poking out was the same: silver, snout-like.

And the fire would be no different – a fire that would kill O. Like Osro's, this Weapon had a roof: a gable of split logs set high on poles. It seemed Kenno too feared the Birdfolk.

The army was smaller than Osro's; about ten thousand men to his thirty. They were armed with swords and spears and bows, and some wore body-armour of hide or metal. Nick could not believe they would match the Hotlanders.

The command tent was pitched upstream from the ford. There a dozen men sat on stools and studied maps spread on the ground. They stared up as the lookouts spotted the Birdfolk. Soldiers ran to guard them, setting arrows in their bows.

'Freemen,' Yellowclaw cried, 'do not shoot. We bring you news of Osro's army.'

'I can't see Kenno there,' Nick said. As they circled closer he made out the fat townsman who had been chief councillor. He wore armour of grey metal, decorated with gold. A helmet plumed with feathers lay on his knees. He made a sign and the bowmen lowered their weapons. A man at his side, a big fellow with a torso like a sea-chest, bellowed, 'Birdfolk, land and speak. You are welcome.'

They landed by the river and climbed to the tent. Soldiers made an escort. They walked with swords drawn and Nick knew it was not ceremony. He still could not see Kenno, but the thin ex-priest was beside the fat man, and he saw with horror that he wore bones about his neck.

'I am Yellowclaw,' the Birdman said. 'Where is Kenno? Nicholas Quinn must speak with him.'

The fat man stood up and put the helmet on his head. He looked like someone setting off for a fancy dress party. But there was nothing comic about his face. 'I know you, Bird. I know the boy. You will speak with deference here. I am Widd, Marshal of the Army of Freemen.'

'Where is Kenno?'

'He is about, somewhere. It does not matter. I command the army. Make your report.'

'I will report to Kenno. No one else.'

'You will do as I order, Bird. Speak out.'

The soldiers stepped closer; and the ex-priest leaned forward and fingered his bones. Yellowclaw stood very still. It seemed he would leap at Widd. Then he sighed.

'Very well. Yesterday we flew over Osro's army. They tried to burn us with their Weapon, but we escaped. They have many warriors, Widd. Enough to make three armies the size of yours.'

'Where are they?'

'North. Eight days at the pace you march. Their way will bring them down the upland plateau by the mountains – you have it on your map. Four days' marching will take you there.'

The officers showed Widd the place. He looked at it, pulling his lower lip, then said to Yellowclaw, 'The warriors, what are they?'

'Hotlanders.'

'How armed?'

'Spears.'

'Our bowmen will make short work of them.'

Yellowclaw shook his head. 'Hotlanders can see arrows in their flight. They pick them out of the air with their shields.'

'Impossible.'

'I have seen it. But none of this matters. Osro has the Weapon.'

'Ah, the Weapon. We have seen his smoke far in the north. It does not tower as high as ours. Our Weapon is better.'

Yellowclaw looked at him flatly. 'Worse,' he said.

'How? That cannot be. These Hotlanders are primitive. They cannot make a weapon to equal ours.'

140

'Osro made it. And I tell you this, their Weapon is better – if I can say better of something evil. Yours is fixed in its turret. Osro's turns this way and that. It points at the sky. He can aim it anywhere.'

The officers fell to whispering; and the ex-priest – Stilgo was his name – sprang forward. 'Lies, Bird. These vermin of the north cannot match our science.'

Yellowclaw looked him up and down. 'You call us vermin too, and we can fly, but you cannot. And you forget, bone-wearer, Osro was a priest, like you.'

'Enough,' Widd said, 'it does not matter. We have this knowledge now, and we shall ambush them. We shall burn their Weapon before it can fire.'

'No,' Nick cried; but Yellowclaw put his wing out and silenced him.

'You will listen now to Nicholas Quinn. He has things to say about this Weapon that you must hear.'

'Children are not heard,' Stilgo cried. His little poisonous eyes burned at Nick. 'Children have no voice in our counsels.'

'He's not a child,' Yellowclaw said. 'He's done more in his life than a dozen men. And you – will – listen.'

'But first,' Nick said . . . He could not bear the sight of the ex-priest any longer. Revulsion overcame him. It seemed that all Susan had done was denied in this man. There he stood, poisonous and evil, with human bones strung about his neck. Nick took one step forward. He seized the thong that held the bones and jerked it down with all his strength. The force of it dragged Stilgo to his knees. Then the thong snapped, and Nick held up the bones and shouted, 'You are free men. Susan ended the rule of the priests. But still you let them wear human bones.' He flung them away over the guards. 'While you have this Stilgo and this Widd you are slaves.'

For a moment no one spoke. Then Stilgo climbed to his feet. His face was grinning. 'Enough, I think.'

'Yes,' Widd said, 'more than enough. The boy is guilty of treason. Take him away, guards. Down by the river. Get rid of him. And kill these Bird vermin too. They are traitors.'

The guards moved, but a voice cried, 'No!' and Kenno broke into the circle, with Limpy beside him. They were muddy and wet from helping at the ford. Kenno put himself between Nick and the swords. 'Stay back. Any who try to kill them must kill me.' The guards hesitated, and Kenno went on, 'I have listened – standing at the back there, I listened. Nick did well to tear off Stilgo's bones. He would not have worn them if I had been here. We got rid of Ferris bones with the Temple. Any who wear them betray our revolution.'

'Kenno,' Widd cried, 'I command here. I am Marshal. And I have ordered death for these traitors.'

Kenno faced him. 'Then kill me first.'

Widd's eyes showed his desire to do it. He would order Kenno's death one day soon – but not now, the time was not now. Kenno saw it. Softly he said, 'You command the army. But I lead the state – for a short time yet. These –' he flung his arm out – 'are my friends. Friends of O. Our debt to them can never be paid. And when they wish to speak, then they speak. So –' deliberately he turned his back on Widd – 'let us hear your message, Nicholas Quinn.'

Nick told it, fast and sure. When he spoke the name of Freeman Wells, Stilgo cried out. Kenno silenced him. When he warned of the death of O some of the officers trembled, but Widd only laughed – and Kenno silenced him too.

'That's all,' Nick said. 'That's what I came to tell you. If you fight, O will die.'

'And if we don't, Nick,' Kenno said, 'Osro will rule. We'll be slaves.'

'I think you'll be slaves anyway.'

'Perhaps we will. But will Osro even spare our lives?'

'He sent a message. Leave your Weapon. Turn back to your homes – and he will consider letting you live.'

'You have spoken with him?' Stilgo cried. 'This boy has spoken with Osro. That is treason.'

'We called from the sky. We gave him the warning we give you. That was his answer.'

'It is treason.'

Widd spoke smoothly, 'It is lies. The whole thing is a plot to make us weak. There is no Freeman Wells, there never was. He is a myth – '

'That's what Osro said. There's nothing to choose between you.'

' – and this girl Susan Ferris, she has interfered too often. Go back to her. Tell her to leave O. If we see her again, or see you, we will carry out our sentence of death.'

'Listen, please – '

'Silence, boy. We are the Freemen. I am Marshal. I shall lead my army north and destroy Osro. I will burn his Weapon. And we shall rule O. We shall bring peace and freedom to the lands of the north. And east, and south. Humans are the ruling kind, and we shall rule. We shall civilize, we shall teach our ways – '

'And get rich. You're worse than Osro. He doesn't pretend to do it for anyone but himself.'

'I'm a patient man. I give you one minute to leave my camp. Take your Birds and go. I will turn my back. If you are standing there when I look round, my guards will have your head off.' He looked at Kenno in challenge, and turned away – a fat man in absurd clothes, but a man of power.

Kenno said, 'Go, Nick. I believe you. I'll do what I can.'

His eyes were dark and empty. There was nothing he could do. Nick raised his hand. He felt he was saying goodbye to all that was good remaining in Freemen. He turned and broke through the guards and the Birdfolk followed. They climbed a hill away from the camp and stood on the summit. Snowflier and Sundercloud spread the sling.

'Here comes Limpy.'

The fisherboy ran up the hill. 'Nick,' he panted, 'is Soona still with you?'

'Yes,' Nick said.

'Give her my love. And my father's.' The arrogant proud Limpy was gone. This boy was frightened. He looked back fearfully as he spoke. 'They will murder him soon. He knows it. So do I. We should have stayed in Stonehaven with my mother.' He blinked. 'They will murder me too.'

'Come with us, Limpy. The Birds can carry two.'

'No. I must stay with him. He can't believe everything has failed. They call themselves Freemen but they are Widd's slaves and Stilgo's slaves. My father won't give up. He'll fight till the end.'

Nick said sadly, 'It's not that sort of fight any more. It's a fight to save O. But good luck, Limpy. I'll give Soona your love. Tell your father she and Susan might still be able to do something. Freeman Wells told them a way.' He did not say it was terrible. Limpy had enough to worry about.

He climbed into the sling. The Birdfolk lifted him, and the boy on the hilltop fell away. Down by the river, Kenno stood alone. The men by the tent had their maps spread out again.

Late in the afternoon, from a hilltop by the sea, Nick saw two towers of smoke far inland. They were many kilometres apart, but their heads seemed to lean and touch each other.

CHAPTER TEN

The Fallen City

The island had not changed in a hundred turns. The beach shone yellow in the afternoon sun as the seals brought the barge in. The bow grated on the sand at the spot where Susan had landed from her glider long ago. She jumped down and walked to the cliff, with Thief at her side. Here, on this warm sand, she had slept. And drunk from a tiny fresh-water spring – she found it again. And peered at the land from the top of the island, making out low buildings in the smoke. No smoke now, and no buildings either. Jungle had swallowed them.

She looked further inland and saw the line of Sheercliff; and Wildwood north and west, climbing into the foothills of a mountain range. She knew this land. In a way it was her land. Back on Earth, it would stay with her for the rest of her life.

She looked down at the beach, where Jimmy and Dawn were bringing gear ashore. The Seafolk were cropping weed in the southern reef – where she had met Island Lover – and Ben and Bess were catching fish further out. She could not see Soona, but heard her flute. She was somewhere under the cliff, and no doubt Aenlocht with her. They were never more than a step apart, tied by the knowledge of what they must do. They were like lovers and scarcely took their eyes off each other. And perhaps there was hatred in it too, for Soona was right; they must do terrible damage to each other. To themselves. And she, Susan Ferris, must help them do it.

Guiltily, as though submitting to some drug, she fumbled

at her throat and drew a little cloth bag from her shirt. She loosened the draw-string and tipped Halves on her palm. They gave her no shock, they were not alive, or not awake; they were sleeping in a death-like sleep that Nick would have a term for – suspended animation? But their perfection made her gasp. She did not know whether it was beauty or strength, form or colour, harmony or line – all of those. They were two and one. They were Humankind. The knowledge of what she held made her tremble. New Halves for old. Changed Halves for those that had done their work too well, and not well enough. In weight, perfectly even. In age – not yet born. A second chance. She closed her hand and held it still. She must not think about it, she must not let her mind run away. See them as ornaments, she said, a pair of ear-rings, a couple of pendants. They would look marvellous dangling from someone's ears. From Soona's ears. The thought made her tremble again. She opened her fingers. Pale amber and plum-red. Tear-drops bending into one another – that perfect shape. And each with its flaw that was no flaw. Her mind started going off again, and she pushed the Halves into their bag and thrust them back beneath her shirt.

Soona's flute had stopped. She and Aenlocht stood out on the sand, looking up at her. They knew what she had been doing. She raised her hand apologetically. Thief butted her thigh. He wanted to go down. He was not happy now unless he had his three charges together.

She climbed down to the reef and crossed the sand. 'How long must we stay here, Susan?' Soona asked.

'Until morning. The Seafolk say the river is silting up. They can't take us up in the dark. And I told Nick I'd wait. I want to hear about Osro and Kenno.'

'They will not listen. Even my father. When will he get here?'

'Soon, I hope. He's had two days.'

'We can't wait long. We must reach the Motherstone before the armies meet.'

'I know.'

Jimmy came up the beach. 'Did you see anything, Susie?'

'It's all jungle. There were buildings there once but they've gone. I suppose the city will be overgrown.'

'Yeah,' Jimmy said, 'an' lousy with rebel priests and runaway dogs and Gawd knows what.'

'We'll be all right with Thief. And Ben and Bess. You'd better go further off, Jimmy. Aenlocht doesn't like it.' As usual when anyone came near Soona, the Hotlander boy had bared his teeth and clawed his fingers.

'Keep yer shirt on, sonny, I'm yer mate,' Jimmy said. He moved a few steps off and said to Soona, 'Yer better play 'im a lullaby. If 'e has a go at me ole Ben'll squash 'im.'

'Don't be angry,' Soona said. 'He knows only what we must do. It grieves him for he thinks he is a traitor to his tribe.'

'Yeah,' Jimmy said, 'me 'eart bleeds fer 'im. I suppose you three know what yer up to?'

'We know,' Susan said.

'Yeah, well – we'll string along fer company, me an' Ben. I guess it's all written down somewhere in a book.'

'Woven in a tapestry,' Susan smiled.

Dawn approached, and the Varg came dripping from the sea. 'What we have to do,' Susan said, 'is go into the city. We have to find Otis Claw's palace. It's fallen into ruins, but we have to find a way down to his throne-hall.'

'Won't be easy. She's all caved in.'

'Once we're there, you'll have to leave us. We have a thing to do – and no one should see.'

'Don't speak of it,' Dawn said. 'It is a human thing and not for Woodlanders.'

'But you guess it?'

'The hint was there in what Freeman Wells said of Humankind.'

'When Nick comes, don't tell him.'

'He will guess too.'

They made a small fire and cooked their food. Bess had caught salmon and they baked them in the coals. Ben brought one for Thief. He ate it, growling with distaste.

The sun had gone down and the western sky was red when Silverwing landed on the beach. 'They're coming. Get food ready.'

Jimmy put more fish in the embers. Sundercloud flew in, and a moment later Yellowclaw and Snowflier came round the cliff with Nick in the sling, hanging his legs through holes, ready for landing. They put him down at the end of the beach. He came to the fire, stretching himself.

'I'm starved. Do I smell fish?'

He ate, while Susan and Soona and Aenlocht watched.

'Now, tell us.'

'There's nothing to tell.'

'Did you see my father?' Soona asked.

'Yes. He's well. Limpy too. They send their love. They're – in some trouble. An argument with Widd. He's in charge of the army. But I think they'll be all right,' he ended lamely.

'They're in danger, Nick. Don't keep it from me.'

'Yes, they are. Widd wants to get rid of them. But if they can last a little bit longer. . .'

'What about the Weapon? Did you warn them?' Susan asked.

'I warned Widd. And Stilgo. They wouldn't listen. Nor would Osro. No one listened.'

'So – they'll fight?'

'Yes.'

'When?'

Nick looked at Yellowclaw.

'In three days,' the Birdman said.

Watcher of Furthermost had come from the sea. Susan looked at him. 'We can land you by the city tomorrow night,' the seal said. 'But you will need a day to find the palace. After that, I do not know.'

'We'll be cuttin' it pretty fine,' Jimmy said.

Later in the night, Nick and Susan walked along the beach and climbed across a low part of the island to see the land. Thief padded uneasily between them. The sky was clear and the stars were bright. The jungle on the shore was black as tar. A fire twinkled down towards the river.

'Hunters, I guess.'

'Or renegade priests. They can't hurt us.'

'They might slow us down.'

'We'll get there, Nick. All I hope is Soona and Aenlocht will be strong enough.'

'And you.'

'Yes, me.' Her hand rose to the thong about her neck.

'What have you got? Something from Freeman Wells?'

'Yes.'

'New Halves?'

She nodded.

'Are you going to turn them into Halfmen again?'

'No, not that. Don't ask me, Nick.'

He was silent. He thought about what Freeman Wells had said – the headlong rush of Humankind, the swamp beast locked in the mind, the Halves out of balance – and things began to fall into place. 'I think I can guess.'

'Dawn said you would.'

'I can see why it can't be just you. It has to be humans from O. They've got to agree. And do it themselves.'

'They know. They've agreed.'

They went back to the embers of the fire. Soona and

Aenlocht were lying in their blankets close to the cliff. Even in sleep their hands were joined. Nick did not feel jealous any longer.

A fine rain was falling in the morning, but it cleared as the Seafolk drove the barge out round the reef. The sea had an easy swell. The crossing would be made in good time. Yellowclaw and Silverwing circled overhead. Snowflier and Sundercloud had gone to scout the river mouth. They came back in mid-morning and reported no sign of life, but further up in the jungle were deserted villages and a camp where a fire still smoked.

'As long as them Pollies are spottin' we're O.K.,' Jimmy said.

The river mouth was blocked by a bar, but the Seafolk ran the barge through a channel at one end and found deep water close to the jungle. All four Birdfolk were in the air, and Ben and Bess had swum ashore and kept pace with the boat, one fifty metres inland, one on the shore. Thief stood on the deck-house roof, scanning the jungle with his yellow eyes.

They came round a bend in the river and found a clearing where crops had grown and a village stood. The houses and the grain fields were burned. Carrion birds rose squawking into the air. At a small jetty a sunken river boat thrust her prow out of the water.

Dawn said, 'Bess has found an old woman in the jungle. She has children with her.' The Seafolk took the barge close to the jetty and Dawn jumped ashore and ran through the sacked village into the trees. After a short while she came back. 'The men were taken for Widd's army. Then a band of outlaws came – bandits and priests – and burned the village, took all the food. They killed the old people and carried off the women and children as slaves. That was yesterday. This woman managed to hide in the jungle with her grandchildren.'

'Do they have food?'

'Enough. They are frightened of wild dogs.'

'Tell them to board themselves in a house. Tell them – one day, soon, the women and the men will come back.'

'Is that true?'

'I think so. People will drift to places they know. Do you think so, Soona?'

'Perhaps,' said the girl. Her eyes were distant. She did not know.

Dawn went back to the jungle and the barge pulled away from the jetty. Soon Yellowclaw lifted the Woodlander girl aboard. The voyage went on, through midday into afternoon. The channel zigzagged from bank to bank. Swamps steamed in the sun, the mudbanks glimmered, creepers and tree-roots invaded the river. Insects swarmed and bit – but Dawn went into the jungle again and made a paste of leaves and gum that kept them off. They passed another village, with nothing alive in it but carrion birds, and once heard a pack of dogs hunting in a swamp. And once someone unseen loosed an arrow at Silverwing, but she was too high for it to strike. After that, Thief prowled in the jungle with the Varg.

Night was coming on when they saw the ruined buildings of the city. Broken walls crept down to the river, sank in mud. They leaned on trees as though grown tired. Fallen roofs lay webbed in creepers. Roots thrust up through pavements and seemed to peer about like burrowing creatures inspecting an upper world. A dozen rotten posts stood in the river. Susan wondered if they were part of the jetty where she had landed a hundred turns ago.

The barge went on. Soon they came to a stone wharf running back to walls rising from the river, three storeys high. Here and there a glass pane glimmered in a window, but most of the wall had fallen out and rooms showed, plundered long ago.

'Here,' Watcher cried from the river. 'Further up it gets too shallow. Tie the barge on the ring in the stone.'

Nick found an old rusty ring and secured the barge. Thief came leaping through the building, ran down the wharf, and made sure his trio of charges were safe. Ben and Bess loped up, and were joined on the wharf by the Birdfolk.

'The city is overgrown,' Silverwing said. 'There's a building here and there above the trees, but most are fallen and the streets are blocked.'

'What about the palace?'

'We saw no palace.'

'But a mountain of broken stone,' Yellowclaw said. 'Black. Overgrown with creepers. There was a giant gate swinging on a hinge.'

'That must be it. There must have been an earthquake,' Susan said.

'An Oquake,' Nick put in. 'Do they have them here?'

'Big ones,' Jimmy said. 'That palace must'a' come down like a dunny in a storm.'

'We saw people,' Silverwing said. 'They haunt the streets, one here, one there. They live like rats in the rubble.'

'How long to get to the palace?' Susan asked.

'A day. You must cut your way through. We would carry you but we cannot carry the Varg, and you must be guarded.'

'We better get some shuteye an' start early,' Jimmy said. 'Susie, you an' yer mates sleep on the barge. Me an' Ben'll doss down in the building so no one can come sneakin' up.'

They ate their food and lay down to rest. Susan and Soona were in the deck-house, with Aenlocht and Thief across the door, one on each side. Dawn and Bess made their beds

152

in the bow, and Nick on the rear deck. The Birdfolk stood sleeping on the wharf.

Once in the night Ben roared in the building, and men fled yelling through the city. And later Nick was wakened by Thief padding by. He heard the soft splash of oars in the dark, and a creaking of rowlocks. But then came a thrashing in the water. The Seafolk had surfaced under the boats and overturned them. Thief added his scream to the din. After that there were no more alarms.

In the dawn the grey mist over the city turned white. Yellowclaw and Silverwing came back from scouting. 'It will lift, but for the first hour we cannot see. The Varg and the Bloodcat must keep you safe. Sundercloud has flown north to the armies. We must know how close they have come to each other.'

'When will he be back?'

'This time tomorrow. What do the Seafolk plan?'

'We will take the barge to mid-river so no one plunders it,' Watcher said. 'If Susan needs us we will be here.'

Jimmy had made a fire in the building and heated food. They ate breakfast sheltered by the walls. 'Listen,' Jimmy said. Out in the jungle dogs were baying, an eerie sound, especially in this building where creepers climbed through windows and threads of mist drifted down stairs that led to nowhere.

'Will they attack?'

'Not if they know what's good for 'em.'

Thief had slipped away. Presently a dog yelped, only once, and not long after Thief was back. He had eaten.

They shouldered their gear. Jimmy put the fire out. 'We gotter keep to wide streets if there's any. Me an' Ben go first. The rest in the middle. Bess can watch the back. I reckon Thief had better scout around.'

Susan made images for Thief and he snarled agreement.

Then Jimmy led them through the ruined building into the city. There had been a yard, a turning place for drays, heavily cobbled, and much of it was clear of growth. But trees in close ranks stood all about. Their heads were in mist. The sun was a fuzzy ball, slanting bars of light through the vapour. Jimmy crossed the yard and forced his way between two mounds of rubble into a street. Creepers leaned from walls. He chopped them with his axe, and Ben tore them, and they went on slowly through the ruins, with gaping doors on either side.

'A handy place fer an ambush,' Jimmy said.

But Thief, peering through doors, leaping on walls, kept up a screaming, and Nick could not imagine anyone coming close. Aenlocht too began to roam about, though keeping Soona in sight. His wounds were almost healed and his agility matched the cat's. The jungle was not his element, but his sharpened sight, his reflexes, seemed to operate as though in the desert. Once he leaped sideways and plucked a hissing spear from the air, and hurled it back where it came from, over the trees.

'They're tryin' long shots,' Jimmy said. But Thief was away after the spear, and nothing more came from that direction.

The mist dissolved. Silverwing floated overhead, with Yellowclaw and Snowflier making sweeps. The lurkers in the ruins would see them too and realize that now they had no chance of lying in wait. They must attack openly or wait for dark.

When the sun was overhead Jimmy stopped. The place had been a city square and like the yard by the wharf was not overgrown. It was paved with tiles a metre square and some were inlaid with images of Otis Claw. His giant statue lay on its back in the middle with an upraised arm broken off at the wrist. His face seemed noble, and that was a lie. So was the inscription on the pedestal: *His fame will live*

154

until the end of time. Jimmy sat on his chest. He sharpened his axe on Claw's cheekbone. Nick took wood from a smashed ox-cart lying nearby and made a fire. It was more for comfort than warmth. A fire in this desolate place was a friendly thing. He rolled a spoked wheel on to it and made it blaze high.

'I don't think I came this way,' Susan said. 'But I came through a square like this.' She remembered a cart hauled by slaves, and Halfmen and women thrusting up their bowls for greasy stew.

Silverwing landed. 'You must go north and east. The black mound is there. But the streets are narrow and the jungle lies thickly over them. We have seen only single dogs, and people in twos and threes. But Yellowclaw thinks they're gathering behind you. They're waiting to see what you will do.'

'Who are they?'

'Ruin-dwellers. People who hunt and scavenge here for food. Untouched by the history of the last hundred turns. The city was a dark place to outsiders.'

'The priests called it the place of desecration,' Soona said. 'There is a pit. Sinners go that way to eternal punishment.'

'I've heard that one before, or somethin' like it,' Jimmy said.

'The pit's the way to the Motherstone,' Susan said.

'You will reach it by dark. You must find a place there to pass the night.'

They ate, and Jimmy led them out of the square, leaving the fire sinking to ashes by the fallen statue. 'Poor old Claw,' Nick said. He thought of the statues of Susan and himself at the Temple. They were broken too. His fame would not live in this world any longer than Claw's. He found the thought oddly comforting. More and more he had the sense of not belonging on O. It was as if he and Susan had been called to do a job – like carpenters or plumbers – and when it was done they would go back home and be forgotten, and their work would be just a part of things. Susan's work, he reminded himself. She was the important one. He did not have much to do any more.

They went through streets in an old part of the city. Shops and houses leaned over alleys too narrow for carts. In places their upper storeys touched, and here and there they had fallen in, making barriers of brick and stone and timber. Creepers twisted everywhere like snakes, and trees were getting a foothold, standing up at shoulder height wherever there was light and space for them. In the shade, in places the sun never came, everything was slimy, fungus-grown. The cobblestones spat water on their ankles. Black pools lay in hollows, with tufts of pale weed at their edges. Insects bit, and Dawn brought out her paste again. It was easy to believe fevers and diseases lived in these alleys. Old yellow bones, rib-bones, pelvis bones, lay half-in half-out of a pond. Jointed fingers gripped a stone. Teeth grinned in a broken jaw. Susan stopped. She shivered.

'I came down this street. There was a murdered man over there.'

'Take it easy,' Jimmy said. 'We must be gettin' close.'

'It looks like thick jungle up ahead,' Nick said.

'That will be the park. There was a creek. A ditch. The palace is on the other side.'

Silverwing shouted from overhead. She led them out of the alley into a clearing where it seemed people had lived recently. Dead fires made patches all about. Jimmy felt one. 'Cold. I wonder where they've got themselves holed up.'

Silverwing landed. 'They are behind, in a half-circle. It seems they like the direction you're going.'

'They're herdin' us,' Jimmy growled. 'How many of 'em?'

'Seventy. Eighty. With clubs and spears.'

'They must want us to go to the palace,' Susan said.

'I don't like it. I'm for havin' a bash at them.'

'We've got to go. Why fight?'

They started into the jungle again. No light came in. The tree-roots were moss-grown and the ground spongy. Soon they came to the ditch Susan remembered but now it was twenty metres wide, stagnant and slimy, and the trees were too thick for the Birdfolk to fly down and lift them over. 'We'll have to swim.'

'It's full of leeches,' Jimmy said. 'They'll 'ave yer sucked dry before yer know it.' He scraped one out with his boot – a slug the size of a match-box, grey, with a patch of yellow gut. 'Get one of these on yer skin, yer wouldn' burn 'im orf with a blow torch.'

'What will we do?'

Jimmy looked at Ben. The old Varg nodded.

'Hop on 'is back. You first, Susie. Don't worry, they won't get through 'is fur.'

Dawn was already on Bess's back, and the younger Varg stepped easily into the water and started swimming, head held high. Jimmy helped Susan up. 'Don't fall orf. There's millions of 'em.'

She knelt and gripped the fur at Ben's neck. His back was as broad as a sofa and though he walked with a rolling gait, in the water only the joints of his shoulders moved. The leech-filled slime slid by close to her knees, but her only worry was that the creatures would find a way through Ben's fur. She glanced back. The others were in a group close to the water. Thief had gone back into the trees. She saw what he meant to do, and though it looked impossible she knew that for him it was easy. He ran to the water's edge and his leap took him soaring over her head, elastically stretched and light as a bird, and down in an arc, over Dawn and Bess. His forepaws splashed in the ooze. A single bound took him clear. He snapped at his leg, where a leech had fastened, and spat it out; then stood waiting for Susan, mewing anxiously. Dawn jumped clear of Bess and the younger Varg turned back. Then Susan was on the shore; and Thief rubbed her once, then prowled the trees.

Soona and Aenlocht came next. Susan saw men moving in the undergrowth, hunched to the ground like animals that searched the mud for food. They darted from tree to tree, dark and dwarf. Jimmy faced them with his axe, but they stayed back, making a soft whistling, a kind of signal. It could be the singing of birds, Susan thought; but coming from the men it was horrible.

Nick and Jimmy came over. Under their weight the Varg struggled to keep their mouths clear of the slime. On land, they shook themselves, and Dawn and Jimmy took their knives and cut leeches from their fur. One had got into the split between Ben's toes and the old Varg watched stoically while Jimmy dug it out. Dawn doctored the cut and they went on. It took another half hour to bring them clear of the jungle.

The space was man-made. Beyond, a wall of stone blocks rose to a shattered top, with an entrance at the end, and half a barred gate, ten metres high. It leaned inward on one hinge, resting on stones, mason-cut, that rose in a tumbled hill towards the sky.

'There, that's it, the palace,' Susan said. Nothing was left of the beehive shape or the chimney that had poured out Otis Claw's poison smoke. It was the gate she recognized. Nick was at her side. 'The ramp must be under all that rock.'

'We're not goin' lookin' ternight,' Jimmy growled. 'Grub's what we need. An' some shuteye.'

Silverwing glided down and hovered. 'We have found a broken place in the wall. It makes a room where you can be safe. Dark is coming. Build a fire. You must be quick.

These jungle folk are gathering.' She flew ahead of them along the wall. They were on a kind of beach, Susan thought, with the jungle as the sea and the stones of the fallen palace a kind of land. The trees were full of flitting shapes, and man-made bird-calls. They came to the hole in the wall. Beams had crashed on blocks of masonry. Sections of wall had tumbled in, and a cave was made – cave more than room – head-high, as large as a double garage.

Thief went in and made sure it was safe. Nick and Jimmy lit a fire at the entrance, building it high with timber from the rubble. They made a barrier half over the door so spears could not be thrown into the cave, but no move came from the jungle, although men watched, some in the open, taking no heed of the Warrior Birds, or Thief, or the Varg.

'They've been herding us, all right.'

'They're a scruffy-lookin' bunch,' Jimmy said.

Nick stood for a while watching them. Men, the whole gathering, not a woman there. Crooked, half-naked, stringy-fleshed. The spears and clubs they carried seemed too large. He supposed they barely kept alive, scavenging and preying on each other in these ruins. Yet there was something dreadful about them. Not their numbers, not their weapons – but their silence, their discipline. It was as though they were engaged in some rite.

He looked into the sky. The Birdfolk were there. Ben and Bess were at the fire, one facing the jungle, the other the mound, so no surprise attack could come. And Thief was in the cave. But still he could not feel safe.

'Nick, come and have some food,' Susan called.

He went in. 'They want us here.'

'At the Motherstone?'

'Yes, maybe.'

'We'll find out tomorrow. If they want us it means there's a way to get down there.'

That did not bring him any comfort. He lay awake thinking of what Susan must do. And Soona. And Aenlocht. He wished there were a part for him to play. If he had guessed right, their task was terrible – the burden of it, the hugeness, made him weak. The threat of the men in the jungle shrank to nothing. He looked at Susan sleeping in the flickering light. It astonished him that she had the strength for tomorrow. And those two, Soona, Aenlocht, sleeping side by side, with her black hair making their pillow – their strength was even more terrible. He dreamed about them spreading out their hands to cover O. He could not tell whether it was life or death they brought.

CHAPTER ELEVEN

Motherstone

It was dark in the cave but outside the unrisen sun lightened the sky. Susan sat up in her blanket and shivered. Aenlocht lay with open eyes, watching her. He spoke a word in his dialect and she guessed it was, 'Good morning'. Soona was still sleeping, with a strand of hair caught in her mouth. It was so childlike that Susan reached out and stroked her cheek. Aenlocht made no move, he seemed to smile, and Susan whispered, 'Look after her.' She threw off her blanket and went outside. Ben was by the fire, almost in the ashes, and Thief was walking back and forth halfway to the jungle, with the untamed regular motion of a tiger in a cage. He stopped and came to her and she scratched him under his jaw.

Jimmy came out yawning and stirred the fire. 'Where's our neighbours?' There was no movement in the jungle, but Susan had no doubt eyes were watching.

'No mist. Are the Pollies keepin' watch?'

They turned in the sky like hawks; but Yellowclaw wheeled north and flapped away, and Silverwing folded her wings and tumbled like a pigeon towards the fire. She braked at tree height and settled lightly.

'Sundercloud is coming. He flies at the end of his strength.'

Nick and Dawn came out, and Bess jumped down from the mound, and they all stared at the sky. Sundercloud came into sight, with Yellowclaw at his side. They made a long, flat landing between mound and jungle, and Sundercloud almost tumbled into the fire as he stopped.

'Today,' he panted. 'They meet today.'

'What time?'

'Osro is on the plain. They must have hauled the Weapon in the night. Widd comes up the valley. Before midday they will be in sight. Already the scouting parties skirmish.'

'So the Weapons will meet.'

'Osro has cleared a line of fire. He will burn Widd's Weapon as it appears. But Widd can make a detour and take him on the side. I cannot tell who will have the advantage.'

'It doesn't matter. It's the same in the end.'

'We better get movin', young Susie. Whatever yer gotter do, now's the time.'

'Yes. We'll go.'

'My father?' Soona asked Sundercloud. 'And my brother? Did you see them?'

'They live. But they walk in chains.'

'All Humankind is in chains,' Yellowclaw said.

'Sure,' Jimmy said, 'but save that fer later. Our cobbers in the bush want us ter move.'

The ragged army was creeping into the open: bare-footed, stringy-haired, with filthy wrappings on their loins and shoulders, and weapons of sharpened wood and scavenged metal. They should have been pathetic but they made Susan's blood run cold. They crept like grey tide-water, bodies bent, faces still; and even Thief did not know what to do.

'They're not going ter clobber us. I reckon they just want us ter move along.'

'Where to?'

'That gate, I reckon. No time fer breakfast. Grab yer things. You Pollies start flappin'. There's nothin' down here you can do.'

They gathered their gear. The Birdfolk leaped into the air – though Sundercloud lumbered – and beat up in circles to where Snowflier still kept watch. The others began their walk to the gate in a tight group, with jungle folk closing in behind. They lined the wall of jungle all the way – hundreds: they had gathered in the night – and others appeared from holes and crannies in the mound. They stood beyond the gate, closing the way.

'Only men. Where are the women?' Susan said.

'Home gettin' the stewpot ready.'

'They're more like priests than cannibals,' Nick said.

'I wish they'd say something.'

'They're sayin' it, in their way.'

'I wonder if they worship the Motherstone,' Susan said. It seemed crazy to be herded, pushed along, to a place they were desperate to reach.

At the gate Ben and Jimmy went in. The others stood by the portal and faced the jungle folk. They stood as though just across a road, and watched without curiosity, but with their weapons forward and bodies crouched. A mouldy kennel smell came from them.

Susan raised her voice. 'You can go away. We're going down to the Motherstone.'

They did not know the word; but stirred and raised their weapons when Jimmy and Ben came back. They sent whistling signals back and forth.

'She's clear inside. They've got a kind of tunnel goin' down.' He looked up at the Birdfolk. 'Keep watch,' he shouted.

'O goes with you. Life goes with you,' Yellowclaw shouted.

'Yeah,' Jimmy muttered, 'that's a big help. Let's go, Susie. Keep in the middle, like before. Me an' Ben first. Bess in the back. But I don't reckon anyone's gunner stop us.'

He led them past the gate and through a canyon in the

rubble. It ended in a tunnel shaped like an O. 'Like a bloddy mouth. We're bein' swallered.'

Soona and Aenlocht joined hands. Susan laid her palm on Thief's neck. We're a cell, she thought, the four of us. She had no thought for Jimmy up ahead, or Nick behind. They were going down to the Motherstone, nothing else was real. She did not worry about the jungle people, or anything that might wait in the tunnel. She, Soona, Aenlocht, Thief, had come together by some law, and nothing could get in their way.

'Torches,' Jimmy said. 'They must'a' lit 'em in the night.'

They were set in rusty brackets on the wall, and made of slow-burning rushes that gave out an evil smell. The light barely spread from one to the next, and became even dimmer when the tunnel sloped and began to turn.

'The ramp,' Nick said. 'Remember, Susan?'

She did not answer. She could think only of getting to the Motherstone. She hardly took in her surroundings, but passed from torch to torch as though each marked a step. But Nick, near the back, was aware of the jungle folk pressing. They never came in sight but their feet rustled, their weapons scraped, and their shadows came creeping on the walls. Their silence still seemed ritual and he was certain now they worshipped something in the pit. Perhaps the Motherstone was guarded by some beast. Anything was possible on O.

He kept close to Susan and Thief. Soon the ramp was broken by fissures. Fractured stone jutted from the walls. A rustling and soft whistling came from the cracks. People moved in there, flattened out like crabs. Arms – or claws – might reach out and touch him.

'How far, Nick?' Jimmy asked.

'We must be halfway. It flattens out in front of the throne-hall. There's another set of doors to go through first.'

'They mightn't be standin' after that earthquake. It looks like this tunnel's closin' in.'

Boulders piled the floor. They climbed to a lamp burning on top. 'There's a hole here, like a slide. They'll 'ave swings next.' It angled steeply down and Jimmy's voice set up echoes in it. Light showed at the bottom but they could not tell how far away it was.

'They got us in a corner. How about you tryin' it, ole feller?'

Ben did not hesitate. He climbed into the chute, almost blocking the entrance, but found more room as he went down. His claws scraped on the stone. He seemed to shrink, a toy bear, and a long time went by before he reached the bottom. They saw him sniff the air and cast about.

Jimmy said, 'O.K. She's all clear.' He climbed in and the others followed. The slope would have set them sliding at any misstep. They felt for cracks and ridges and Thief and Bess held on with their claws. It took a long time, and wore their knees raw, but at last they scrambled out; and found themselves in the tunnel again, with rubble piled to the ceiling at the back of the chute. A torch burned on the wall. The way ahead was fractured into steps.

'We must'a' come three or four levels,' Jimmy said. 'They sure do their best ter keep it open.'

'What time is it?' Susan asked.

'I'd say we got half an hour.'

'The Motherstone's close. I can feel it.'

'The light around the next bend doesn't come from a torch,' Soona said.

'So we made it. But I think I hear our mates comin' down. I'd just as soon not have 'em. I reckon Ben an' Bess can cork this hole.'

The Varg saw what was needed. They rolled stones from the rubble and piled them at the opening from the chute.

Then they shoved a large flat boulder on the top, jamming it hard, and the hole was closed. In a moment clubs beat on it, iron scraped, but the boulder was firm.

'They won't shift that,' Jimmy said. 'Now let's 'ave a shufti at this Mummystone.'

'No,' Susan said. 'Just me and Soona and Aenlocht. And Thief.'

'We'll let yer do what yer hafter. But there might be someone lickin' 'is chops down there.'

'We'll come until we see the Motherstone,' Nick said.

Soona leaned on Aenlocht. 'We must hurry.' Her face had gone dead white, and the Hotlander, fierce in his paint, put his arm around her and held her up. He too seemed uncertain on his feet. It was as if they were drained of strength and kept on moving by an act of will. Thief pushed Susan.

'All right,' she said. 'But once you've seen, stay back. What we have to do is just for us.' She did not wait for Jimmy but pushed ahead. The tunnel turned and another rock pile stood in the way. The light came from the top through a narrow hole. It made none of the flickering of the torches, and spread with an even-ness beyond the power of flame. Yet it was faint, almost accidental, and Susan remembered how the dome of force about the Motherstone had seemed to keep its light to itself. Soona and Aenlocht came to her side.

'We go up there. Through that hole.'

'Quickly, Susan, quickly. If I am to do it I must do it now.'

'Stay close to me.' She climbed the rock pile to the light. Thief went half a step ahead. He thrust his head into the hole, then wormed his body through. She saw him standing on the other side, and heard his mew of wonder. She crawled into the hole and came out beside him on a ledge and saw what it was that astonished him. The Stone. The

Motherstone, the globe of light. It was far below, in a basin on the throne-room floor. Just like it was a hundred turns ago, Susan thought. Everything had changed, but not that: the grey stone, shaped like an office desk, with the golden apple enclosing it. She remembered how the light had hummed like bees when she stood inside, and how it had seemed to have the sweetness of honey – and how the Halves had fused into the Stone in a crackle of fire. She could not see them, but they were there. They would always be there, until O ended. Or until someone came, wearing the Mark, and lifted them, and changed them for new. The bag about her neck seemed to weigh like lead.

'Is that it? Is that the Motherstone?'

'Yes, that's it.' She had not heard Soona come to her side, but she took the fishergirl's hand; and Aenlocht's on her other side. They seemed to form this pattern naturally: the Knower, with the Pale One and the Red One flanking her.

Nick and Dawn and Jimmy crawled through the hole, but the Varg were too big. They would never see the Motherstone.

'We're up by the ceiling,' Nick said. 'The doors must be blocked. Otis Claw's throne was over there. The last time we saw this place it was full of Halfmen.'

'There are bones around the light,' Dawn said.

Jimmy was peering down. 'There's ridges for climbin'. She's pretty hairy.'

Susan heard their voices as though from a distance. They seemed to have nothing to do with her. She had already seen the way to go. One of the buttresses was split and jutting edges made holds for a descent. Thief went first. He was delicate and sure as a mountain goat and in a moment reached the empty floor. He gave a call. Aenlocht and Soona went next. The throne-room seemed very far away, but Aenlocht guided the fishergirl. They clung, they stepped, angling back and forth, and stood at last by the Bloodcat, looking up at Susan.

Her fear of heights made her tremble, but this climb was easier than others she had made, and she lowered herself and found the first ridge with her toes.

'Take it easy, Sue. There's no hurry,' she heard Nick say. How did he know? Already Osro had his Weapon aimed. The battle might be only moments away. She climbed fast, not looking down, keeping her eyes fixed on the stone in front of her face. It was coloured by the glow from the light and her shadow moved on it not like an ordinary shadow but as though penetrated by colour. After all these turns, the light seemed to recognize and reach out for her. She imagined she felt warmth on her back.

She climbed round to the side of the buttress and saw a deep angle by the wall. No light reached in and she looked away from it quickly, knowing she would fall if she entered. Across the face she went, moving with care, and angled back. She came near the shadow again, but this was the last time. One more traverse and she would be on the floor with Thief and Soona.

The Bloodcat screamed a warning. She did not know what it was for. He leaped up the buttress but found no claw-hold and fell back. Something she mistook for a snake came darting out of the angle at her throat. It made a gleam in the shadow, it was white and long and angular, and she thought it was going to bite. She let go her hold, and understood too late it was an arm, the head and fangs were hand and nails. They tore her face and ripped her shirt. Then she was falling.

She seemed to turn over, and heard her scream following her. Aenlocht and Soona came zooming up – but that was illusion, she was falling, and somehow they were under her. She felt the jarring of bodies, and fists that seemed to punch

168

all over her. The fishergirl and the Hotlander boy had moved as though a single brain controlled them, and Thief had moved, all three with the same explosive speed, and come between Susan and the floor. Her weight crushed them. She burst through their arms and struck at hip and thigh on Thief's rib-cage. Then all four lay tangled at the foot of the buttress. Susan was stunned, she could not see properly, was aware of their faces flashing at her; and then of other faces, boiling out of the dark, of yellow bodies rolling like a stream, and pale mad eyes. She heard Thief scream and Aenlocht give his fighting cry, and saw them strike, and blood leap out and splash the stone, and felt Soona dragging her back. Then she was on her feet, yelling too. 'The light! Run for the light. Aenlocht! Thief!'

They moved in a knot, all four together, running towards the basin in the floor where the light shone. The people followed – women old and young, bent and quick, silent except for the scraping of long-nailed feet on the floor. They held make-shift weapons: shards of stone, spikes of wood. More came from holes and broken corners of the throne-hall. They were the dwellers in this place, they were the guardians of the Motherstone. This was what the jungle men had been herding them to.

Susan came to the edge of the depression. The floor sloped down to the base of the dome, ten metres away; but she stopped. The basin was filled with bones. It was like the remains of some huge cannibal feast. She understood: this came from a hundred turns of sacrifice. These people, these dark-dwellers, worshipped the Motherstone as a god, and brought it offerings: animals, people. They flung them against the light, where they burned as Otis Claw had burned. His charred bones must lie at the bottom of this heap. It sickened her. Everything on O seemed to turn to evil.

She swung round to face the women, these hideous priestesses of their god, and held up her hand. 'Stop!' They were ten paces back, pressing in their hundreds, and setting up at last a soft anticipatory cackle. But they stopped, and leaned towards her, and pulsed and breathed like a single organism.

'Stay back,' she said. 'You don't have to throw us to your god. We came willingly. We will offer ourselves.'

They hissed, they throbbed, they shivered with dread and desire. But they held their place, ten steps back. Little broken murmurings and cacklings ran through them. What Susan offered was something new. One said, 'The God is hungry. He has not eaten since yesternight.'

Susan looked down. There were bones of every sort, human, animal, bird, even fish – and some, she was sure, were children's bones. She thought of them herded down, and given to these women, and hauled to the dome. And thrown against it. After that, what remained of their flesh was eaten. There was no trace left on these bones. The sour stink in the hall came from the living not the dead. She had no doubt that what she was about to do was right.

'Soona? Aenlocht?'

'Yes. Let us go.' The fishergirl held herself very straight. 'Stay back,' she said to the women. 'We will give ourselves to your god. But I promise you – we are the last.'

'Go! Go! He waits.'

'Come on,' Susan said. 'Stay with me. Stay close, Thief.'

She took Soona's hand and Aenlocht's hand. Thief put himself behind her, with his head brushing her leg, and they started for the light. Bones rolled greasily under their feet, and snapped and settled. The women lapped round the basin, leaning inwards. But Susan had no fear of the light. It had welcomed her once and would welcome again. The evil was out there, in the women.

She reached the light. It curved up and over. The Motherstone sat grey and neutral in the centre – and she saw the Halves, just as she had placed them long ago. They made a little pool, two colours, clear as water.

'Are those the Halves?' Soona whispered.

'Yes.' She tightened her grip on Soona's hand, but the fishergirl did not falter. Aenlocht too showed no uncertainty. Only Thief was disturbed. He turned his head at Susan and made a snarl.

'It's all right, Thief. I have the Mark. The light will welcome us.' She sent him an image of them standing inside the dome. Then she said, 'Keep hold of me. All step through together,' and she sent a last look back at the women, almost a message, telling them that their time was over, and warning them of what was to come.

The bones lay almost chest high outside the dome. Going down was like jumping down a bank. They did it without hurry; and heard the women scream with disbelief. Then they were inside and the noise was a murmur. A downy warmth wrapped round them, and a sweetness penetrated their skin and filled their lungs. Soona and Aenlocht held each other, Thief sank on his haunches and purred. But Susan looked back and raised a warning hand at the women. They had come crawling over the bones and looked in with their mad yellow eyes. Their mouths howled, their teeth gleamed; and one, in her fury, clawed the light and burned in a flash of fire. Her blackened body fell on the bones. But the others did not retreat. They glared in, howling – like ghosts at a window, Susan thought.

She turned away. She could not face them. She felt at her throat for the Halves. And then her cry filled the dome, it filled the throne-hall. It was a cry of anguish and rage and despair. Gone! The Halves were gone. The hand striking from the darkness had robbed her. The Halves had been torn from her throat, and there was no way to get them back.

Nick had seen the arm dart out like a snake. Saw it strike: saw the treasure it returned with. Susan fell. It was over in a second. Aenlocht had her, she was safe. So he forgot her, he let all his energies concentrate on the Halves, and before he had made any decision, found himself halfway down the buttress. Jimmy was coming awkwardly behind, and Dawn had taken a different way. She reached his side as he angled down the ledge to the darkness where Susan had been struck.

'Someone was in here. Someone got the Halves.'

'Careful, Nick.'

He took no notice, but hauled himself in and stood in a crack splitting the wall. A dim light showed at the end. He thought he heard a scuttling in the dark.

'They're in here.'

Jimmy arrived. 'Let me go first, Nick.'

'I can go faster.' He saw something blur the light, and hauled himself along the crack sideways like a crab. He came out in a cave. A reed torch burned on the wall and he wrenched it out and held it high. Dawn came to his side, and Jimmy crashed out on his hands and knees and stood up cursing.

'People live here,' Dawn said, pointing at bits of cloth, implements of stone and wood, lying against the walls.

'It's a doss-house,' Jimmy growled. 'But I reckon they're all out there chasin' Susie.'

'Listen.' A scuttling came from the dark. 'One of them isn't.' Nick pushed the torch ahead, and went forward fast and cautiously. More nests of rag and rubbish where the women lived and slept. The cave bent. Another torch burned on the wall and Jimmy took it. They came to alcoves chipped in the walls, with hangings over them, and Nick ripped them down, exposing dens fitter for animals than humans. All were empty. He began to give up hope. This cave could go on for miles and the woman they were chasing must know every corner. She could be hiding in any one of these tangles or rags and rubbish. He began to tear and kick them.

'Nick, be quiet.' Dawn was crouching, listening. 'She's there. Ahead of us. She's reached her home. I hear her panting.'

She took the lead. The cave was wider than a street. She led them to the far side, where more hollows were curtained off with rags. A panting, a hoarse whimpering of greed and fear and delight, came from one; and Nick pulled the curtain aside, and there the woman squatted in her hole. She was not old; but sallow, withered, venomous, greasy with the droppings of her food. She glared at them and held her hands tight knotted under her chin. The broken draw-string tangled with the hair falling to her waist.

Nick stepped in and held out his hand. 'Give them to me.'

She spat at him. Saliva wet his face and he wiped it with his arm. 'We won't hurt you. All you've got to do is to give them to me.'

'Easy son, she'll bite yer,' Jimmy said.

'We've got to get them. Susan can't do anything without them.' He put his hand forward and the woman struck at it with her teeth. 'The God-stones, the pretty God-stones, they are mine.'

'They belong to the god,' Nick said. 'He sent me for them.'

She did not hear. Her hands were clasped so tightly they would never come apart.

'Yer won't get them that way,' Jimmy said. 'An' I don't feel up ter givin' her a whack. Out of there, Nick. Me an' Dawn'll try the Varg way.'

'Yes,' said the Woodlander girl, 'stand outside. When we give the word, come in slowly and take the Halves.'

Nick backed out of the alcove. Dawn and Jimmy stood one on each side, and the woman fixed her eyes on Jimmy and snarled at him. 'That's it, look at me,' Jimmy said. He lowered his head and swayed it back and forth like a Varg. Then Dawn made a move, sudden, quick, and the woman swung her eyes, snarling again; and Dawn stopped, and set up an easy motion of her head. Jimmy moved . . . and so it went on, until the woman was mesmerized. Then Dawn whispered, 'Now, come in slowly, no sudden moves. She won't see you.'

Nick crouched. He came sidling into the alcove and the woman's eyes, fixed on Jimmy now, seemed to look through him. He knelt in front of her.

'Open her fingers. Take the Halves.'

He pulled her arms down like a lever, forced the fingers back one by one, and took the bag, feeling the Halves sliding under the cloth.

'Now go. Out of sight. She will be crazy when she wakes.'

Nick turned and picked his torch up from the floor. He ran back through the cave and found the crack and edged along it. A shriek of grief and fury came from behind him. Dawn came sliding down the crack. 'Jimmy has let her go. Hurry, Nick. She will fight like a Bloodcat.'

He came out on the buttress. Down in the throne-hall the cave-dwellers thronged about the light. They blocked his view of the Motherstone, but he saw Aenlocht and Soona, with Susan held between them, and as he started climbing he yelled to her, 'I've got them, Susan. I've got the Halves.' He had no idea how to get them to her. Dawn swung up beside him, and Jimmy scrambled on to the buttress and started climbing. Then the woman burst out. She tore at her face with her nails. Her cry cut through

174

the throne-hall like a cat-shriek. 'Stones! They have my God-stones. Pretty stones.' She lunged at Jimmy, missed her grip, and fell wailing to the throne-hall floor.

'Up yer go, youngker,' Jimmy yelled. 'We're in trouble.'

The priestesses were streaming back from the dome, flowing across the floor like a muddy tide. They lapped about the base of the buttress, and some began to claw their way up.

Jimmy stood beside Nick and Dawn. 'I can hold 'em. They gotter come one at a time. But I dunno how yer gunner get them doodahs down to Susie.'

Nick looked at the dome. The three in the light might as well be miles away. But he saw Susan's face as though she stood in front of him, and read the grief on it, and knew he must not fail. There was no way to get through that mad throng. They would tear him to pieces. But there must be some trick he could think of, some bit of cunning. 'Use yer loaf.' Had Jimmy spoken or did he dream it? He saw Thief standing in front of Susan, lashing his tail – and suddenly he had it: he would call someone the women would never catch.

He reached down by his feet and found a stone. He stood up straight, shielding it in his hand, and thrust his fist out. 'Here they are,' he cried, 'here are the God-stones. You can have them.' He swung back his arm and hurled it away, far out to the left of the dome. The cave-dwellers ran after it. Some of those on the buttress tumbled off. He waited until the way was clear, and yelled to Susan, 'Now. Send Thief,' and sensed that Dawn was calling silently, calling the cat.

Thief burst from the dome. He crossed the bones in one stride and came through the throne-hall like a sun-flare. Nick waited. The bag must not fall on stone. He waited until Thief was below the buttress. Then he held his arm out and let the Halves drop.

Susan saw them fall and saw Thief catch them in his mouth. Then she lost sight of him as the women boiled back and closed him in. But she knew nothing would stop him. She saw the flash of red as he leaped. He went a quarter way up the buttress and propelled himself out, all in one motion, and twisted in the air, and came down clear of them, and loped round the rush they made, out to the side of the dome, and started in.

'It will burn him,' Soona cried.

'He has the Halves. It will welcome him.'

He bounded over the bone-pit, put his head in, seemed to grin, with the draw-string trailing from his jaws.

'Thank you, Thief. In you come, quick.'

She took the bag. She did not look at the cave-dwellers again, but smiled at Soona sadly, and at Aenlocht. 'Are you ready?'

They nodded, did not speak. She tipped the Halves into her palm, hearing the drawn breath of the two who must hold them. She put the lighter Half on the Mark on her wrist, and quickly, deftly, set the other beside it. She felt a tingling, an itching, but ignored it. The Halves came to life: one burning gold, the other red. Their radiance made a light about her brighter than the light that bathed them all.

Slowly she put her arm out, offered it. 'Soona. Aenlocht.' They seemed blind. Their hands were clasped, her right in his left. They were trying to be brave, but Soona had to whisper, 'Will it hurt?'

'No, Soona. No pain of that sort.'

They took the Halves, did not choose, each took the nearer one. And gasped. And swayed.

'Hold them now. Keep them safe. I do the next part.'

Distant shouts came from outside. She paid no more heed to them than sounds in another street. She turned and faced the Motherstone. Thief came to her side and she was glad.

She touched him on the head. Then she reached out for the Halves – the old ones, returned there in the time of Otis Claw. They were fused in the rock, making a circle, red in one part, gold in the other. Neither seemed more strong or had more life than the other. There was no sign that in the human struggle evil had won. In any case, she had no time to consider that. She wanted just to do what she must do, so Soona and Aenlocht should not wait.

She laid two fingertips on the Halves, and saw the thread of light run round the edge, and through the S dividing them. They were unfused, freed from the Motherstone. She picked them up and held them in her hand.

There was a kind of sighing in the throne-hall, a rustling as the cave-dwellers sank on their knees, turned on their sides, sank in sleep. All about the dome of light they lay, and Susan knew that part of it was done: in the north, on the plateau, the armies slept, Widd and Osro, Stilgo, Kenno, Limpy – Hotlanders, townsmen, ex-priests. The Weapons were standing with no one to use them. Except for Soona and Aenlocht, and the three from Earth, all of Humankind on O were sleeping. And they would sleep until Halves, old or new, were placed on the Motherstone – or until they died. But death was not a part of Freeman Wells' plan.

Susan fumbled with the bag. She put the Halves inside. She did not know what she would do with them. She felt a pain like betrayal when Thief padded from her side and stood with Soona and Aenlocht. But that was right. She had done her part. The rest was theirs, O was theirs. She stepped slowly back to the edge of the light.

Soona and Aenlocht approached the Motherstone. She could not find a word for where they were going. It was not death. Yet it was a kind of death she watched.

Tears ran on Soona's cheeks. Aenlocht's face was twisted

177

with fear. She saw how white their hands grew with the strength of their clasp.

'Goodbye, Susan,' Soona said.

Her voice choked as she answered, 'Goodbye, Soona. Goodbye, Aenlocht.'

They placed the Halves. The thread of light ran round, ran through; and Soona and Aenlocht fell to the ground. They curled up in a ball, legs and arms clenched to their bodies, faces still. They slept, or were in a kind of death.

How long they lay, Susan could not tell. She knew that she had clambered out of the dome, and crossed the bones, and time had passed. She had crouched with Dawn and Jimmy and Nick at the foot of the buttress. Perhaps she had eaten food, she did not know. Now they were back at the light. Nick was holding her.

'Are they waking up?'

'Yes. They're moving.'

'They won't be anyone we know.'

All about, the cave-dwellers were stirring. And in the light the fishergirl, the Hotlander boy, uncoiled from where they had fallen, and climbed to their knees. They opened their eyes and looked about, and wailed with terror at the strangeness of the place they found themselves in.

CHAPTER TWELVE

A Last Look At O

'The armies are dispersing,' Yellowclaw said. 'They have laid down swords and spears and they drift away in groups, north and south.'

'They do not know what swords and spears are for,' Silverwing said.

'What about the Weapon?'

'Two Weapons. They sit there on the plain, facing each other. Widd went round to take Osro on the side. But Osro saw. The turret was coming about. I cannot say who would have fired first. Now – they sit there. Woodlanders dismantle them. Birds will fly the parts to a cave, and Stonefolk will take them down to the Deepest Place. That will be the end of the Weapon.'

'Did you find Limpy and Kenno?' Susan asked.

'Yes. Still chained. We freed them. Some instinct draws them south.'

'They'll go to Stonehaven. But what will they do there? They won't know what boats are for.'

'They'll survive,' Dawn said. 'Woodlanders will watch over them. Humankind will be our children.'

'They'll be growing up for hundreds of thousands of years,' Nick said. He remembered the bodiless voice of Freeman Wells. 'For aeons.'

'He's made a place for them to rest in, Nick. He's given them a chance to beat the swamp beast.'

'I suppose so.' He looked at Soona and Aenlocht, walking ahead on the forest path, with Thief between them. 'They don't remember who they were.'

'That was the price. They were chosen – but they chose.'

'Soona knew where she was going,' Susan said.

'She's not really Soona any more.'

'No, she's not.'

'She's – primitive. At least in her mind. Neanderthal.'

'That's just a word. They're children again, that's all we can say.'

'Yer gettin' morbid,' Jimmy said. 'They're bloddy lucky ter be alive. All of us is lucky.'

'The Birdfolk will help them,' Silverwing said. 'Woodlanders will help. And Stonefolk too. All the Folk.'

'Just leave 'em alone. They'll make their own way. Let's 'ave some grub.'

They had come out of the throne-hall, out of the city, up into Wildwood. It had taken six days. They travelled slowly, keeping watch on Soona and Aenlocht. They had to be taught the simplest things, how to wash, how to dress. They seemed to think clothes were a part of themselves and fought against having them taken off – and once they were off, would not put them on. Simple implements they understood: a stick for poking, a stone for scratching. Their language was a grunt, an exclamation. Soona's face was pale and beautiful, but her eyes lit up only with the simplest understandings. Inside, she was – Nick looked for a way of saying it – back with the monkeys. He had to struggle not to draw away. At night she and Aenlocht slept in the ferns. He supposed they would start having children soon. That was a good thing – a new generation. That was the start of the long climb back. He hoped when they got there it would be something different, otherwise all this was a waste of time.

But when he climbed a hill and looked at Wildwood and saw the trees stretching to the sea and the mountains rising, he knew it had been no waste. O was saved. He began to feel that Soona and Aenlocht, Osro and Widd, had been very lucky. They had a second chance. He began to wonder if he really wanted to go back to Earth.

They followed the Sweetwater. Jimmy and Dawn and the Varg would turn south at the foot of the mountains. Nick had no idea what Soona and Aenlocht meant to do. He wasn't sure they could think of tomorrow. As for Thief, he was a mystery. Nick kept well out of his way.

'Is Thief still your friend?'

'Not so much now,' Susan said. 'I'm not really part of O any more.'

'Will he stay with Soona and Aenlocht?'

'I don't think so. He's too wild. He'll go to the Hotlands. But I think he'll remember. He knows what they did. He'll come back and see them now and then.'

'Will they stay in one place?'

'No, they're nomads. They'll wander. Maybe up north, Aenlocht's land. Or down to Stonehaven. Places will draw them, but they won't stay. It'll be thousands of years before humans learn to have homes.' She smiled at him. 'But I know a place they'll come to now and then.'

They went into the foothills. The mountains climbed in steps into the sky; and it was time for Jimmy and Dawn to turn south.

'Don't go startin' anything, young Susie. This time I'm not comin' back.'

'There'll be no one hiding in the cave.'

'Better not be. I wanter put me feet up fer a while. I reckon I've earned it.'

'You have, Jimmy . . .'

'No waterworks, eh. We had some hairy times, an' some good times. You an' me an' young Nick here. Let's just think about them now an' then.'

'Yes. All right.'

181

Dawn had found Shy flowers. She gave them to Nick and Susan, and looked at the scratches on Susan's face. They had healed, but a pale scar would show on her cheek. They said goodbye. Then Dawn and Bess and Jimmy and Ben crossed the river. They looked back from the trees on the other side. The Varg stood on their hind legs and roared. Dawn and Jimmy waved. Then they went south, and Nick and Susan knew that they would never see them again.

'Don't cry, Susan.'

'I can't help it. There's nothing wrong with it. Waterworks.'

'No, I guess not.' His own eyes were wet. 'What are we going to do with Aenlocht and Soona?'

'Come with me. I think they'll follow.'

They climbed up from the river, over a saddle, and came to a spring in a basin of hills. Nick had not seen it before. He thought it was the loveliest place he had ever seen.

'This is what Jimmy named for me.'

'Susan's Spring.'

'Just Susan.' She looked at Aenlocht and Soona, standing side by side, and thought how well the place suited them, where water sprang fresh and cold from the depths of O. 'There's a cave in the hill up there. They might stay a while.'

'And come back?'

'Now and then.' She left them standing with Thief and went to the shore. Nick followed her and watched while she took the bag with the old Halves from her shirt.

'They'd make a good pair of ear-rings.'

'They belong here.' She held them for a moment. The whole thing had come down to this – two coloured stones in her hand. Two new people by a spring.

She threw the Halves. They flashed in the sun, and skipped on the water. Then they sank. She turned away and went to Soona and Aenlocht.

'We're going now, me and Nick. This is your place if you want it.'

They looked at her blankly. They could not understand.

'Soona, I've got something for you.' She reached into her shirt and took out the flute. 'It belonged to someone I knew. Another Soona. Now it's yours. Listen, I'll show you what it's for.' She put it to her mouth and blew a note. Soona sprang back and Aenlocht shielded her. But Susan blew again, and again, and seemed to see a movement of interest in their eyes. 'Take it, Soona.' Gently she took her hand and coaxed the fingers open. A look of pleasure showed on Soona's face as she felt the carved stem. She did not try to put it to her mouth but held it in her hand and smiled. She would never play it, a single note, it was too soon. Perhaps her children – or someone ten generations away – would make a sound with a simple reed, music would be born. But it seemed important that this Soona should have the old one's flute.

'Now, Thief.' The Bloodcat came forward. She knew that he had moved away from her. There would be no more passing of images. But he let her place her hand on his head, and he rubbed himself once against her thigh. 'Goodbye, Thief. You don't have to have a name any more.' The Bloodcat lay down in front of Soona and Aenlocht.

'He'll stay with them a while.'

Nick and Susan walked up to the rim of the basin. When they looked back Soona and Aenlocht were by the trees, breaking open a rotten log for grubs. Thief was drinking at the spring.

'They'll be all right.'

'Yes. Come on, Susan. It's getting late.'

They went up through the hills on to the mountain, and all afternoon climbed to the plateau. Now and then Birdfolk

183

dipped in their flight to call goodbye. Silverwing and Yellowclaw landed and embraced them.

It was dusk when they came to the cave.

'We'll go back to the day we started from.'

'Nick, do you remember when we went home before? We got a story ready.'

'Why our hair was longer. Why our clothes were torn.'

'And nobody noticed. We didn't need to say anything.'

'They'll notice this time.'

'We're different people.'

They took out their Shy flowers and held them on their palms.

'This time we'll tell the truth.'

'They won't believe us.'

'We'll tell them anyway.'

They joined hands and approached the cave, and turned there, and stood a while, for a last look at O.